Acclaim for The Yogi Leader

"An innovative approach to leading authentically with mind, body, and heart built from the ancient wisdom of yoga and well-known leadership theories. The stories are captivating and follow seven different leaders who use *The Seven Elements of Leadership* to impact their families, businesses, and communities."

Marshall Goldsmith, Ph.D.
New York Times #1 bestselling author of *Triggers, Mojo, & What Got You Here Won't Get You There*
Thinkers 50 #1 Executive Coach for 10 years
2-time *Thinkers 50* #1 Leadership Thinker in the World

THE
YOGI LEADER

"The Yogi Leader makes the ancient wisdom of yoga relevant to our modern lives today. It can help you become a better leader, and more important a better, healthier, and more fulfilled human being."

Tal Ben Shahar, Ph.D.
Co-Founder, Happiness Studies Academy

"Adding leadership elements to the practice of yoga is simply brilliant! From the health-conscious enthusiast who wants to find a deeper state of being to the overworked corporate executive needing to silence the chaos around them – The Yogi Leader is the book for you."

Doug "Dr. Luff" Luffborough, III, Ph.D.
President & CEO, Higher Level Leadership, LLC

"An inspiring book with compelling stories which provide strategies to improve your leadership; Leila Naderi and John Franey illustrate how to unleash your leadership potential through reflection and meditation."

Paula A. Cordeiro, Ed.D.
Dammeyer Distinguished Professor of Global Leadership & Education, University of San Diego

"This book provides both practical and meaningful strategies for embracing the anxiety of leading in the world today and ensuring you develop the courage to engage the world productively and creatively. The principles presented apply to leading and also to life. I highly encourage leaders who want to enjoy leading to read this book."

Gil Brady, Ed.D.
Founder, Relationship Impact

"The Yogi Leader is engaging, and the message is accessible in the forms of narratives which help the to-be-successful-leader to relate and get insights into the aspects of their own personality and belief system that prevent them from being an effective leader. The references to Yoga postures, breathing and relaxation teaching, plus self-affirmation and positive thinking techniques, are opening people to the empowering aspect of Yoga as a holistic body-mind-spirit practice. The book is a contribution to our confused, scattered time when often times people find themselves with no voice and no vision."

Swami Sitaramananda

"A compelling read for authentic leadership enthusiasts, indeed! Dr. Naderi and Dr. Franey remind us that compassion and empathy in business and in life are needed more than ever and that you can succeed and lead with your heart and your head together in harmony."

Andy Vaughn
President & CEO, Alliant International University System

"Naderi and Franey have woven the elements of yoga into the everyday practice of leadership. These principles can help leaders at all levels improve themselves and their ability to lead."

Mark Blankenship, Ph.D.
Executive Vice President, Chief of Staff & Strategy
Jack in the Box, Inc.

The Yogi Leader

Discovering the Seven Elements of Leading with Mind, Body, & Heart

Leila Naderi, PhD
John J. Franey, PhD

To: Alden Domini

Wishing you all the best in
2020 & beyond.

Leila Naderi

Published by

The Leader Mill, LLC
Ramona, CA
www.theleadermill.com

ISBN: 978-0-9974605-3-7

Dedicated with LOVE and GRATITUDE to my family, especially my mom (Parvin) and my siblings (Soheila, Fara, Faty, Reza, and Hassan). Many thanks to my brother, Reza, whose entrepreneurial leadership and positive impacts at Mirrella Tile inspire me every day!

With sincere gratitude to all of my teachers, mentors, and friends across the globe including Dr. John J. Franey, my professor and co-author of this book.

Dr. Leila Naderi

For my longtime mentor and friend, Lea, who always knows just what to say, even when I don't know what to ask.

Dr. John J. Franey

Table of Contents

Let's Begin with Lotus Pose

Some of you are thinking… *Oh no, not another self-help book.*

Or you're thinking… *Not another book on how yoga is amazing.*

Or you're thinking… *Not another book on how to be a leader.*

Or you're thinking… *What did my friend get me into when she said I had to read this book on my vacation?*

Or you're thinking… *Why did my boss assign this book for reading this year as our professional development?*

Don't worry, you won't hurt our feelings with these thoughts, as we often think the same thing when we start a book like this. But what if we told you there was something special about this book… *Gee, where have I heard that one before… oh that's right with every self-help book I've ever picked up.*

No truly and honestly. This book is different, it's not like those other books… *Sure, next you'll say I'll win the lottery too!*

Well no. We won't promise you'll win the lottery, but we bet this book is different than all the other books you have read… *Oh, I've got to hear this! What's the catch?*

No, no… no catch at all. Just something very different and organic and elemental by nature. Something you haven't seen before. Something you haven't heard before. Something that will definitely catch your attention… *Okay either you are incredible writers and can sell anything to anybody or… you actually have something innovative and interesting.*

Well thanks for the compliment… but we guarantee it's not because we can sell anything to anybody. It really comes down to a simple, yet complex concept. As you probably know, there are hundreds of books out there on the individual topics of leadership, yoga, and self-help… *You're definitely right about that!*

But wait for it… here is the really cool innovative part. What if we told you there was a book that weaved all three concepts together into an emotional journey of leadership development through yoga practice (hint hint… we're talking about this book right here that you are reading)… *Mind blown… things just got very interesting! You have my attention. Now what should I know as I go into this book?*

You, like most people, probably see yoga as a practice for improving flexibility, generating calmness, building health, reducing anxiety, and so on and so on. You hear it's a healthy way to exercise. You hear it's good for your mind and body. Doctors tell you to do it. Your friend swears by it and how it makes her feel. YouTube videos talk about how yoga is so impactful. Facebook memes celebrate how amazing you feel when you do yoga. But what if we told you it can be even more than that? What if we told you that yoga can actually help you to be a better leader... *Are you serious? No way. Totally different things. What does yoga have to do with leadership?*

This entire concept of yoga for leadership began through the doctoral dissertation research work of Dr. Leila Naderi (who holds a Ph.D. in Leadership). As an advanced Hatha / Sivananda yoga instructor, Dr. Naderi was fascinated with the concept of the relationship between yoga practice and leadership. She noticed an incredible synergy and correlation between the two concepts. Her doctoral study found that leaders who practice yoga regularly score higher on authentic leadership skill tests than leaders who either don't practice yoga or rarely practice yoga.

It was a truly interesting finding that warranted a deeper dive into how yoga can be instrumental in supporting and promoting leadership development. That is where Dr. Naderi's friend and leadership development consultant, Dr. John Franey (who also holds a Ph.D. in Leadership Studies), came into the picture.

As Dr. Naderi and Dr. Franey worked through the concepts of yoga and leadership, they realized that the chakras of yoga (chakras are spiritual energy centers that exist within particular areas of the human body) and various leadership approaches were in fact extremely synergistic. From this synergy emerged the concept of **The Seven Elements of Leadership**, each of which is perfectly aligned with a chakra of yoga practice. Each of the elements is a different skill that people need in order to lead effectively and authentically with mind, body, and heart in any aspect of life.

This book then is really about discovering who we are as people… and more importantly who we are as leaders. It is built out of well-known, research-based leadership theories and approaches. It is built from yoga practice that stretches back thousands of years. It is built out of the reflective nature of yoga and the opportunity to improve ourselves through reflection, meditation, and mindfulness.

The Yogi Leader is not about one single leader, but rather it follows the stories of seven different leaders, each with their own set of problems and issues to deal with in their leadership practice. Each of their stories focuses on a different Element of Leadership, and thus a different chakra. You'll recognize the stories because they are stories about you. You'll recognize the struggles they face as struggles you face. You'll recognize their emotions as emotions you have. On this journey, you will get to know each one of them and realize that you are a part of them, and they are a part of you.

It begins with **Salma**, a young woman who finds out she is now the head of her non-profit's marketing department, but she is overwhelmed, panicked, and worried about whether she can take on such a massive new leadership role.

Then there is **Alden**, the founder of a startup tech company, who has always worked best by himself and struggles to connect with others, but now is forced to work with a team of his employees to launch their newest app.

And how about **Taylor**, who is fed up with her current career and starts her own health and wellness company, but is struggling to fill so many roles as a one-woman business and doesn't know what actions to take to move forward.

We can't forget **Miguel**, an old school construction company CEO, who is making tons of money, but there is something more important than money missing in his life, his leadership, and his company.

We turn to **Shantel**, a teacher in a low socio-economic neighborhood, who recognizes a major issue at her school but is afraid to speak her voice because she doesn't think that anyone would listen to a teacher.

We get to know **Rebecca**, a working mom and human resources manager, who is struggling to figure out who she really is in life. She is trying to be everything for everyone and yet is losing her identity in the process.

And finally, we connect with **Lea**, a lifelong yogi and instructor, who has spent her entire life trying to help others but is struggling to understand whether her work has had the impact she hoped for in the world around her.

Each of these people have a Yogi Leader within themselves, just waiting to be discovered. Yogi Leaders use The Seven Elements of Leadership to lead authentically with mind, body, and heart. They are the type of leader we want to be. They are the type of leader you want to be.

These are their stories. These are our stories.
These are your stories.

These are their lives. These are our lives.
This is your life.

The Momentum Element

Salma stood staring into the bathroom mirror. She was freaking out. Panic had set in. Beads of sweat were welling up on her forehead. Her face was flush. Her heart was pounding. Her breath was stuck in some sort of staccato hyperventilation. She was trying to calm herself down...

> Breathe girl. It's all good. Just breathe. Slow down. It's all good. Keep it together. You can do this. Keep it together. Just breathe. You can do this.

But Salma felt like passing out. Her hands grasped onto the countertop as she ducked her head and stared down into the sink. She had to keep it together or someone was going to find her crumpled up on the floor of the bathroom totally passed out. It's one thing for that to happen when you're partying with your roommates in college, but not such a good thing at work. Definitely not at work. Her fingers started a rapid tapping on the countertop. It was like taking the fastest Beethoven concerto and speeding up the rpm's by like a thousand. She splashed a little water on her face which seemed to cool herself back down. She looked at herself in the mirror, but all she could see was fear staring right back at her. Her inner voice was trying to stay calm…

What is up with me? I should be happy. Pumped up. Ecstatic. This is what I've always wanted.

A Facebook post Salma had seen the night before popped into her mind. At the time she thought it was just another dumb thing she had found during her mindless social media surfing. The post had talked about some study that said the human body feels excitement and anxiety in the exact same way. It made sense that her body might be feeling excited… I mean this was a huge moment. She knew she was super excited, but she definitely felt a whole heck of a lot worse than when she was usually excited about something.

She tried to smile at herself in the mirror as she told herself, "It's okay, this feeling is not fear, it's excitement." She repeated the statement a few more times. But it didn't matter what Facebook had said, because she just wasn't believing it in this moment. It wouldn't be the first time that social media was wrong. Her body knew. Her mind knew. She was scared. She was overwhelmed. She had finally reached what she had dreamed about since she had arrived at the non-profit a few years ago as a college grad. She was achieving that which she had worked so hard for. She was being recognized for her talent, skills, and abilities. It should have been all good...

But was it too much? Was it too quick? Am I actually ready? Can I actually handle what is ahead of me?

What lay ahead seemed massive... immovable... maybe even impossible. There was no way she could take on so much. It all seemed so daunting. The bathroom started spinning around her as she closed her eyes...

You've been right where Salma is right now. Well maybe not exactly where she is in terms of standing in the work bathroom having a panic attack (although that might have been the case for you as well). But you have felt this panicky feeling in your life before... probably multiple times. It usually comes from the feeling of being overwhelmed by something in your life. Maybe it's when your mom's health started to slip in her older age. Maybe it's when you faced that new health and fitness plan you set for a New Year's resolution and weren't sure if you could actually do it. Maybe it's when you weren't sure how you were going to pay the mortgage that one summer. Maybe it's when your son fell off his bike and ended up in the emergency room.

No matter what the exact situation was that you faced, you know that feeling of the world seeming to crash around you. It's the feeling of claustrophobia, when the walls of the room seem to be closing in around you. It's the short quick breaths where you can't seem to fill your lungs. We assume that it's always brought on by bad news or bad situations that we find ourselves dropped into. But this isn't always the case. These bad times tend to stand out because we can sense the panic coming on and feel it leave when everything is fixed.

Think about getting on a roller coaster. Unless you're an absolute adrenaline junkie, you will be feeling that panic as you slowly shuffle through the line to get on the ride. The level of panic rises with every bend in the line, each glimpse of the coaster as it goes screaming overhead on the tracks. Then as you turn that last corner and see the loading area, you reach the moment of crazy panic. Now remember how Salma mentioned the Facebook meme that said excitement and anxiety manifest the same way in the human body. This is actually true (we know it's shocking to hear something on Facebook is true… right!). So, as you start to climb into your seat on the coaster, it's almost impossible to figure out whether the feeling you're having is excitement or anxiety. In situations like this we almost automatically believe the feeling we are having is fear-induced panic and anxiety. It can't possibly be excitement… we're afraid of the coaster for sure. There's no way we're pumped up about this ride.

Salma automatically recognizes the fear and anxiety in her body… but what if it's actually excitement? How could that be you ask? Simple. Before she ended up in the work bathroom freaking out, she had been called into a meeting with her organization's CEO. Her old boss, the director of the marketing department, had retired weeks before. The old director had spurred on Salma to apply for the position. Despite Salma's hesitations about not being ready or old enough or experienced enough to step into the position, she respected her boss so much that she had applied for it.

In the meeting that morning with the CEO, Salma had received the news she was being promoted into the director's role. It was amazing. It was exciting. It was like a dream. And yet minutes later, she found herself in the bathroom freaking out. Was it anxiety or was it excitement? Could it be both? She was so excited to be moving up in her career, but she was also overwhelmed having realized what was in front of her. Think about your own life and how hard it is to read the messages your body and mind are trying to send you. Ever feel totally confused and like you're going to lose it all? Yeah, now you know where Salma is…

The rest of the first day in Salma's new role flew by in a daze of congratulations from colleagues, conversations with people who needed her to hear their thoughts on what was wrong with the department and packing up her desk to move into her new office. With every conversation she had, it only reaffirmed how much there was to this new role. Instead of being able to center on her individual role or project within the larger department like she had before, she was now going to be a part of everything that was happening in the marketing department. Late in the afternoon as she was trying to just keep her head above water, her phone chimed with a text message. She glanced down and saw the message from her friend Hannah:

Can't wait to see you for our yoga class! 😊 😊 😊

"Oh crap!" Salma said out loud. In all the excitement of the day she had totally forgotten about the yoga class. Her hands went to her forehead as she started to rub her temples…

How did I forget the yoga? And of all days it has to be today. I don't think I can do it. I should skip it.

Her friends had been pressuring her for a while to join them for some yoga after work. But yoga wasn't her thing. Her friends were total yoga people, going to classes all the time. They loved it and swore by how much it helped them. But Salma had never been an overly athletic woman. Even as a kid she hadn't ever liked PE or sports. It just wasn't her thing. In college she had gotten into working out in the campus gym, but that was mostly just cardio work on treadmills and stair climbers. But yoga seemed so overwhelming. To Salma, yoga was sooooo athletic.

But Hannah and the other girls had talked Salma into it, with a promise to go for drinks after class. When she had agreed to it earlier in the week, Salma told herself she needed to get out and try some new things. But now with the news of running the marketing department, she wanted to ghost her friends. She was already panicked about work as she had barely kept herself from passing out in the bathroom. The last thing she needed to happen was to freak out on a yoga mat in front of her friends. But they were too good of friends to ghost. Plus, it might be nice to have a reason to move on from the workday. She knew she would at least get to share with her friends the great news of her promotion.

A few hours later she found herself parked in front of **Lea's Life Studio**, a little hole in the wall type of place. It didn't look anything like she had imagined a yoga studio looking like. She had seen all these fancy yoga studios in shows like every Real Housewives ever invented. But this studio didn't look anything like that. It seemed small. It seemed homey. It was quiet. It was simple. It was rustic. It was beautiful. It was comforting. Even with the relaxing look of the studio in front of her, Salma was sitting in her car feeling that anxiety rising back up just like in the bathroom earlier that day...

> What if you look like an idiot? What if everybody sees that you don't know what you're doing? No way you make it in that class with real yoga people…

Just then she heard a tap on her car window, and she looked up to see Hannah's cheerful face. Behind her were the rest of their friends carrying their yoga mats and water bottles…

> Here goes nothing. Just get through it. A nice cold glass of rosé is awaiting as soon as this is over.

Minutes later she found herself seated on a mat in the front of the class. Salma would've preferred the back of the room, but her friends insisted. They were regulars and loved to be up front. They swore to Salma how amazing the teacher was and they didn't want to miss anything she had to say.

As Salma looked around the room to take in the studio around her, she found that it perfectly aligned with the outside façade. The studio was small, homey, quiet, simple, rustic, comforting, and beautiful. For a moment Salma felt at peace. There was no busyness in the room. It was simplistic. It was a perfect refuge for the craziness of work and her day. After checking out her surroundings, Salma took her gaze back down to the floor in front of her hoping to not draw any more attention to herself. She figured everybody there knew she was new to the class. Plus, she had so much to think about with the new job. That overwhelming feeling was sitting right there on the mat with her. Then she heard, "Hi there… how are you doing?"

> Oh crap… I knew I'd stick out. Would it be weird if I just turned and ran the hell out of the room? I can't do this. Not today of all days.

Salma looked up slowly to see a little old lady sitting cross-legged in front of her. Salma had been so lost in her thoughts about work, she hadn't even noticed the lady come over and sit right in front of her. The older woman wore loose fitting, stretchy white pants and a bohemian style white shirt. Her salt and pepper hair was cropped short tucking in just below her ears in a cute little pixie cut. She had the type of face that made you just want to smile. But Salma was wrestling with so much anxiety and panic from work that even though she wanted to smile at the woman, there was a part of her that just wanted to run for the door and never look back…

> Smile at her. She looks like a nice lady and seems so friendly. You can do it. But what if I can't hack it here? There's the door… no stay and try it out. I could just get up and leave… maybe if I stay this would be good for me. Maybe I should make a run for it…

The fight or flight complex is innate to our humanity. We deal with this on a regular basis. It's a choice based on safety and survival that goes way back in our DNA. It's the most basic of crises we work through in our minds. It's why Maslow puts survival and safety as the base of his Hierarchy of Needs. When faced with a situation that seems to interrupt our basic safety (although not always about dealing with a dangerous crisis), we work through our options deciding if it's better to retreat and live to fight another day (flight) or to take on the situation in the moment (fight). We can't possibly deal with anything else in our lives if we can't solve issues with survival and safety first.

While neither Salma nor any of us in this situation are *literally* dealing with true survival situations, our brain is telling us "I don't want to be in this situation because I am uncomfortable." All of us have been here at many different points in life. It might be the uncomfortable conversation in the lunchroom at work that you don't want to be a part of. It might be the career move that you aren't sure is the best for you. It might be your post on Facebook that you aren't sure how others are going to react.

In all of these situations, we are fighting a battle within ourselves trying to deal with the fight or flight complex. In this case, Salma is hypersensitive to this situation because of what is going on at work. She is struggling with fear and anxiety so even a benign situation like this one in the yoga studio has now turned into a manifestation of the fight or flight complex from work. The door is always nearby for us in these situations. It's calling for us to run away from the discomfort and fear and anxiety. The door is open, but does it really offer the respite that we think it does? Will it really make the situation any better? Maybe in the immediate moment it will... but not likely in the long run.

The woman smiled sweetly at Salma and asked again, "How are you doing?" Salma tried to twist her lips into some sort of smile, but it was hard with everything on her mind. "Uhhh... good. How are you?" Salma replied. The woman smiled. "I'm fine, but it doesn't seem like you're really solid with your answer of *good*." Salma's attempt at a smile slipped away. Was it that easy to see her struggle? Hannah jumped in, "Hey Lea, this is our friend Salma. We've been trying to get her here forever, and she finally came with us."

So, this was the Lea of Lea's Life Studio. Salma had heard a ton about this woman from her friends. They were always singing her praises. Yogi. Therapist. Leader. Teacher. Friend. Mentor. Superhero. "Welcome to our abode, Salma," Lea calmly replied. "Have you ever done yoga before?" Salma shook her head no. Lea smiled again, "No worries. You're probably scared. You're probably anxious. You're probably nervous." Salma smiled in relief, "Yeah, all of that and more." Lea placed her palm on Salma's forearm and in a soothing tone said, "There is nothing to fear in this room. You aren't the first to be nervous. You aren't the first to be afraid. But I promise there is nothing to fear. Can I give you a word of advice for getting started on this journey?"

Salma nodded her head. Lea leaned in closer and said in the smallest whisper, "Don't get overwhelmed by *all* of yoga. You are not going to be able to do it all today. You won't be able to do most of it today. The path is far too long to be walked in a single session. If you think about all of yoga at this very moment it will freeze you in fear. It is impossible to grow when you are frozen. So instead of thinking about all that is in front of you in the world… at this moment, focus instead on each small step. Focus on one single breath at a time. Focus on one single move at a time. Focus on one single step at a time. One breath, one move, one step." Lea smiled and walked away. Hannah leaned over from her mat, "See what did we tell you? She's amazing, right!"

What Lea was noting with her words of advice was the notion that when we focus on too much at one time, we are going to get overwhelmed. The whole picture is too much to take in. It is massive. It is more than we can handle. But this is where we are apt to go with our thought processes on a regular basis. We think on the massive scale instead of the minimal scale. We focus on the massivity of what lies ahead which just snowballs the fear and anxiety that is apt to hit us with anything new. For so many of us, the fear of not reaching the end makes us quit before we even get started. At least that way we won't fail, right?

It's like taking a long car ride across multiple states for a vacation. If you only focus on the end of the path, then it's never going to feel like you're going anywhere. No matter how far you go, the end will still always feel so far away. When you are taking a trip like this you have built up the idea that the reward of your journey lies at the end of what will feel like a never-ending road. You'll feel great at the very end, but the rest of the trip feels like a slog of the same scenery over and over again.

A perfect example of this is when you take kids to a cool place like Disneyland. Let's say you usually only get to go there once a year, so there's a ton of excitement built up into the trip. Let's say to get to Disneyland takes a 2-hour drive from your house, but for your kids it feels like forever. It's the long drive filled with all of the age-old questions from the back seat, "Are we there yet? When are we going to get there? Are we ever going to make it? I have to pee!" When your kids are really young, they are bummed out the entire drive because they never think you're going to get there. It feels so far away because all they can think about is what lies at the end. Then that moment hits when they see the Matterhorn above the skyline and suddenly all the worry and anxiety is gone. They are in pure joy and excitement. As your kids get older, they begin to change the way they see the trip. While they're still focused on the end goal of a day spent meeting Mickey and Minnie, riding coasters and eating way too much food, they begin to recognize spots along the drive that mean they're getting closer. They cheer and get excited when you pass certain buildings or landmarks or stores that they know are on the way to Disneyland. What they don't realize is that they have broken down a seemingly impossible distance into manageable chunks they know they can reach.

We are all like Salma when faced with something new and seemingly difficult in our lives. We tend to only look at the end, which overwhelms and leaves us fearing whether we can truly get there. Thinking about all of yoga and how good others are at yoga would be intimidating. But Lea was able to break down the massivity of the path that lay ahead into small chunks that were much more manageable. And it made all the difference for Salma and her fear of yoga.

Salma was lying in the perfect peaceful quiet position on her mat. She was lying on her side all tucked up having come out of her Corpse Pose that felt so good. She felt like a baby in a mother's womb. It was so comforting. It was so peaceful. She felt like she could just fall asleep there and be good for hours. Her mind was going over the phrase that Lea had shared with her about *one breath at a time… one move at a time… one step at a time.* She kept repeating it to herself in her thoughts. The phrase was so calming and reassuring.

Salma felt a nudge at her elbow. She slowly opened one eye to see Hannah leaning over her and giggling, "Hey, so this is kind of the end of class. We're supposed to leave!" Salma sat up slowly, only to find the room basically empty. She had been so lost in what Lea had called Shavasana, Salma hadn't realized the class was over. "See I told you Lea and her classes are life-changing. Now let's go get that drink." Salma glanced over at Lea who was standing near the door of the studio talking to other students. Salma knew she had to talk to Lea again. "Can I catch up with you girls in a little while. I need to thank Lea," said Salma. Hannah and the others left to head over to the wine bar while Salma made her way over to Lea, who was now standing near the exit.

"I just wanted to say thank you Lea," said Salma happily, "Your advice really helped me. I was totally scared of this class. Especially after the crazy day I had at work. I didn't think I could handle it, but when I focused on each move and each breath it seemed to make sense. I still can't do most of what you showed us tonight, but I wasn't scared. I kept telling myself one step at a time. And it worked." Lea smiled, "I am so happy to hear that. We will see you again, right?"

"For sure," said Salma before shrinking back at the thought of her work. "I mean I hope so, unless work overwhelms me." Lea smiled and leaned in closely, "Remember... One breath at a time. One move at a time. One step at a time." Salma shook her head, "No, no I was talking about my work stuff..." Lea put her palm on Salma's arm again and said, "I was talking about your work too... One breath at a time. One move at a time. One step at a time."

As Salma walked to the wine bar, she wasn't quite sure if Lea had understood there was a difference between what she was dealing with at work and what she was feeling about the yoga class. I mean how could she give advice about work troubles if Salma hadn't even told her about the situation...

How many times do you find yourself trying to compartmentalize all the things that are going on in your life like Salma? She can't possibly see any connection between her work panic and the fear she had walking into yoga. We do this all the time, telling ourselves that we only have an issue in one part of our lives. But in reality, it is extremely difficult to compartmentalize and not let issues in one area bleed into another area. Think about the times you get pissed at someone or you get into an argument with a spouse, a parent, or a co-worker. We narrow down our reasoning to whatever happened in that very moment. But usually when we get pissed off or argue it's because of something much deeper than the immediate matter that set off the argument.

Think about how at work you might get upset in a meeting with your colleague Bill because he is talking on and on and on. It feels like the entire meeting is about what he has to say. You just want to get a word in and so you get short and frustrated and check out emotionally and mentally. You are ticked off. Your entire body language changes. You might speak more sharply or go completely quiet. You're off your game. But think about it, most of the time that Bill talks, you just let him go on and on and on. You know that's the way he is and usually you let it go because typically it's no big deal. But on this particular day, you are pissed.

What changed? Bill always talks forever and ever and ever, so why today are you suddenly upset? Most likely it's because something else is going on in your life. Maybe you got cut off by a jerk driver on the way to work. Or your kids' school called that morning and told you that your daughter had been in an argument with another kid. Or maybe your boss had called you into her office to tell you that one of your clients had decided to go with someone else for their services. Whatever the reason, you're clearly carrying some heavy baggage with you into that meeting with Bill. In this case, Bill isn't the actual issue for you, but rather your pain in one area is brought on by something bigger and deeper than that single moment. For Salma, maybe if she had come to her first yoga class on another day where everything was awesome in life, she would have been happy and excited. But in this case, she was down, she was panicked, she was worried. And she carried all of that with her into that studio. So maybe Lea's advice was spot on... not just for tackling the yoga class, but for Salma's life as well.

After getting drinks with her friends, Salma returned home to sit down and relax after a long day. She called her parents on the phone to share the big news of her promotion. They kept telling her how proud they were. Salma could hear the excitement in their voices. It was the same excitement she had heard from her friends over drinks as well. Everybody was so excited for her. Hearing how happy they all were at the news, Salma didn't want to bring them down by sharing about how she had actually reacted to the news while at work. She didn't share about her escapades in the bathroom or how it felt like her new office was spinning around her at one point in the afternoon. Let sleeping giants sleep she had told herself. Why ruin the happiness by sharing how scared she was? It was obvious that they all believed in her.

As she sat there with the TV droning on through some reality dating show, she found herself thinking about what Lea had told her about the one breath, one move, one step at a time. She couldn't shake it from her head. She fell asleep on the couch thinking about that advice and how she could use it at work. Lea had said it for a reason, so it had to mean something more than just learning some yoga moves.

The next day as she arrived at work, Salma was greeted with piles of file folders and spiral bound workbooks stacked throughout her office. She hadn't even had time to decorate her new office and it was already filling up fast with work. It brought her back to her first week in the company... a fresh-faced young college grad hoping to make a difference through the non-profit. She remembered how overwhelmed she felt with the first project she was ever assigned to in the marketing department. She was totally freaking out back then and now as she looked back, she realized how tiny and insignificant that moment seemed now.

Through a conversation with the CEO's assistant, Salma learned that the pile of work in her office was all the stuff from the old director. All the different projects that the marketing department was working on either currently or planning to work on in the future. When Salma returned to her desk and looked around at all the stuff, the panic came rushing back at her like a flood down a valley when the dam breaks. The room was spinning around again. She was short of breath. Her head was killing her…

Hello overwhelmed. Hello panic. Hello breakdown. Why did you have to show up again today?

Salma wanted to run back to the bathroom. She wanted to escape. She wanted the old director to stop her retirement. It was Salma's first full day in the new position, and she knew she was in for a long road ahead. But the thought of the long road triggered something inside of her. She suddenly saw Lea smiling at her. She could hear Lea's voice say, "One breath at a time. One move at a time. One step at a time."

Salma suddenly became aware of her breath. Salma breathed in and out slowly. The hyperventilated staccato breath that had been rising up went back to a slow steady breath. She felt calm in the face of panic. She felt peace in the face of anxiety. One step at a time. First step was to head down to her first meeting with the department. She knew she could do this first step as she had been to plenty of these meetings, just never as the leader of the group. But she could do it. She could take this step just like Lea had said. She picked up her notebook from the desk and strolled out of the office. She focused again on her breathing as she walked…

You're ready girl. One breath, one move, one step.

As she walked into the meeting room, she noticed her team was there and staring right at her. She became very aware of her movements and her thoughts in that moment...

What are they all thinking? Do they think I shouldn't have been the pick for the job? Do they think I can't handle it? Are they wanting to take my place?

Just then the entire group stood up and started clapping for her. She instantly smiled. Everybody was so happy for her. They were pumped up and excited. After she got them all to stop, she got started with the meeting. The next hour was filled with various team members sharing their projects and talking through what they had on their plate. Salma was quickly realizing again how many different projects there were to get done in this department. And more importantly, how many people felt their project was the most important one in the group. How was she going to figure out which should take precedence over the other ones? How was she going to get all these projects done?

That overwhelmed feeling was sinking in again. She spent the rest of the afternoon trying to figure out how to take all of this on without sacrificing one project for another. She didn't want anyone to think she was playing favorites. Maybe she could do all of them at the same time. That seemed impossible. She knew the overwhelmed feeling was turning her brain to mush. She couldn't concentrate. She couldn't think clearly. She couldn't figure out what to do next.

This happens more often then we can count in our lives. As we pile more projects, more work, more things, onto our plate we become overwhelmed by the enormity of it all. Our brain struggles to comprehend how to get through. Our brain also plays tricks on us. It tells us we can't possibly get it done. It confuses us by throwing out different scenarios. If we start thinking about one thing on our list, then it throws out a situation where we let something else go because of this choice and *everything* falls apart.

Imagine the following scenario as an example of this debilitating conundrum. You are a ten-year old kid and your family has decided to go out for dinner to a new buffet joint because all the kids can get plenty to eat and for a cheaper price. A win-win for everybody right? (well not for the foodies in the group who probably want a fancy meal, but remember you're 10 years old, so you probably aren't thinking about that in that moment). You walk into the buffet restaurant and your eyes go huge. You've never seen so much food in front of you in your life. Not even at Thanksgiving is there this much food on the table. As you walk down the serving tables to get a plate and start filling it up, you are amazed. Each step brings a new favorite item into your sight. Each step makes you even hungrier. You have no idea where to even start. You basically want to eat everything that is out there... (well, maybe not all the different veggies since you are only 10 years old)!

You watch your teenage brother start piling up his plate with everything. The plate is a heaping pile of fried food and carbs, so heavy and out of balance he probably needs a forklift to get it back to the table. You watch your older sister go through and take one spoonful of a bunch of different items so she can try everything before deciding on what exactly she wants to eat. Let's not even get started on your little brother who comes out with an entire plate of Jell-O (which upsets your dad because he isn't getting his money's worth). As you go through the meal you are watching how everybody makes it through the meal. It takes big brother forever to get through all the food on his plate, most of which went cold as he was eating because he took too much. Your older sister went back after her sampler platter and took a second helping of a handful of items that she really wanted to eat more of. Meanwhile, little brother got most of the Jell-O on the floor beside him rather than in his mouth.

By the end of the meal, big brother has gorged himself into oblivion, unable to have any dessert because his meal was a disaster. He left the restaurant and is lying in the car because he is so sick. Little brother stuck with his Jell-O which completely wasted his chance to eat some cool new foods because he was scared to try anything he didn't know. Older sister looks totally happy, because she saved room for a great plate of desserts. She tried a bunch of things, focused in on those she liked the most, and had a great time.

So, what's the point of this story? What does a buffet dinner have to do with Salma's issues at work? Simple. Just like Salma and the mountain of projects in front of her at work, your siblings faced the same situation, an overwhelming amount of options. Everyone has a choice in how they go at an overwhelming situation. Try to take on everything at one time like big brother and you'll end up sick in the car and feeling miserable. Focus only on the easiest thing like little brother and by the end you will not have challenged yourself or really accomplished anything (or as your dad says, you would have wasted the opportunity and his money). Sample a bunch of different things then pick a few items of greatest importance like big sister did, and you will find yourself feeling good in the end. But can Salma do this at work?

Unlike her first yoga class, Salma couldn't wait to get back for her second session. She was ready to leave work behind and find some solace and peace of mind in the studio. As the session began, Salma couldn't help but think about the one step, one move, one breath advice. How could she incorporate that into her work and life? She set the thought aside and focused on the new poses that Lea was teaching. Salma found that while she could do well with certain poses like the Mountain or Tree Poses, she was struggling to switch from one pose to another. The sequences were confusing. She felt like she was in a game of Twister and her body was all tied up in knots while trying to keep from falling. She was trying to think two or three moves in advance, but all it was doing was confusing her even more.

At one point, Lea walked by her and leaned in to whisper, "Don't worry about all of the moves at once. Focus. One breath. One move. One step. Focus. One breath. One move. One step." As with the first session, Lea knew just what to say to her in that moment. Salma stopped worrying about all of it and instead focused her mind on each individual pose…

Mountain Pose. Stand up. Straighten up. Shoulders back. Feet. Ground. Power. Strength. Happy. Relaxed. Breathe. Move. Step. Good.

Salma could feel her body connecting with the ground below her. It seemed to send strength right up through her body. She felt so good. She felt she could do anything. The session went much better after that. She no longer worried about keeping up with everybody else in the class. She only focused in on her next move. As class came to an end, she found herself again wanting to talk to Lea. There was something pulling Salma to hear more from the old yogi. "How did it go?" Lea asked. "Much better after I refocused," chirped a happy Salma, "If only you could come to work with me. I have so many things to try to figure out that I am completely lost." Lea smiled again, "You don't need me to figure this out. All you need is you. All you need to remember is one breath at a time, one move at a time, one step at a time."

"Yeah, no that's great for my yoga, but it ain't that easy at work. I have a hundred projects. A team of people. A ton of directions to move in. It's so much harder…" Salma stopped mumbling when she felt Lea's hand on her arm. "Yoga. Work. Home. Life. It's all the same. Life can be simple or complex. It is what you choose to make it. The question is which step do you need to take first?" whispered Lea.

That night back at home Salma found herself sitting in the lotus position, legs crossed and hands on her knees. She was lost in thought. She was trying to make sense of Lea's words in terms of her work. She kept thinking about how much she was struggling in class trying to go through the entire yoga sequence. Thinking about the sequence was overwhelming, which made thoughts of failure flood Salma's mind. But when she focused on a single pose, she felt confidence. And with each new pose she completed, she felt momentum growing. But how could this help her at work?

Which step do I take first? Which step do I take first? How can I use this? What did she mean?

And then it came to her. What she was dealing with at work was the same thing she was dealing with in terms of the yoga sequence. She was looking at her new leadership role as a massive whole item, something she had never done before, the same as how she saw the yoga sequence. This is where the panic and fear and anxiety were living. But if she broke down her new leadership role then she would find that it was just a compilation of dozens of projects she had already been successful at in her previous role as an employee.

Salma knew she was damn good at projects. That is what had moved her up into her new role. She had to stop focusing on the whole big new leadership role and instead break it down into smaller, more manageable projects where she and her team could succeed. And with that she slept peacefully for the first time since she had gotten the new role. She knew exactly what she had to do. She was ready to take it…

One breath at a time. One move at a time.
One step at a time.

Salma was facing what so many leaders face in their leadership roles. The mission or job or goal is so massive and long term it brings on that overwhelming feeling. Looking all the way down the road to the big end goal for our leadership can leave us frozen. The best example of this is with our health goals. Let's look at two options and see which one you would be more successful at.

The first is that your doctor tells you at your annual physical she wants you to lose 50 lbs. in order to be healthier and fix your blood pressure and cholesterol issues. She will check in on you at your next annual physical and expects it to be done. You know how important it is for you to lose the weight. You know what you need to do to accomplish the goal. But 50 lbs. seem so impossible. Plus, it's a whole year until the doctor's going to check on you again. You think you don't have to start right away because you have an entire year to get it done. At a certain point you will hit the moment where you ask yourself, "What's the point in trying since it'll take forever and I'm not even sure I can lose 50 whole lbs.?"

The second situation is that your doctor tells you the same message about losing the weight. But this time, she tells you she wants you to lose 5 lbs. and to see her in two weeks. You leave that visit feeling pumped. Five pounds in two weeks is nothing. No problem at all. You return to see her, and you find out you lost 8 lbs. instead. She tells you what a great job you've done and that she wants you to lose another 5 lbs. by the time she sees you again in two weeks. You are pumped up because you already did this once and you know you can do it again… hello momentum… so nice to meet you!

Of course, the second situation is much more likely to be accomplished than the first. When you can break a big goal into smaller manageable chunks, you provide an opportunity for success. Plus, the smaller, more manageable goals along the way allow you to build momentum and confidence with every step you successfully complete. Think of it like having to run a mile. Let's say we told you to go and start running a mile through a country field and we'll stop you when you're done, but you aren't able to track how far you're actually running. You have no idea how far you have gone or how much you have left. You're going to feel the urge to quit. You won't know when to push your speed or balance yourself out. But let's say we have you run on a school track and say you have to run four laps (one mile). Imagine how much more successful and faster you'll be able to go when you can track your progress and feel more confident and accomplished with each lap that you complete.

This is the **Momentum Element of Leadership**. It is the first element of being a Yogi Leader who leads authentically with mind, body, and heart. It's perfectly aligned to the first yoga chakra, the earth chakra, which concentrates on being grounded, rooted, balanced, and stable on our feet. The Momentum Element is all about a leader setting forth a path towards a shared vision of success with smaller, manageable goals along the way. The idea is as simple as it sounds.

As leaders, we want to set up smaller goals that our team (our followers) can reach. Not only does each step get us closer to the end goal, but each step is an opportunity to celebrate an accomplishment and build momentum. And yes, we absolutely need to celebrate, or at least recognize, each accomplishment. And each step we complete, we feel momentum gaining and confidence building. We are ready to take on the next step no matter how hard it may look because we know success.

This is the Momentum Element of Leadership that Salma has figured out will work for her situation. Just like the yoga routine where Lea helped her to see it as a series of individual poses that she could do. The whole big mission seems a lot less impossible when we can break it down into more manageable chunks. Momentum builds as success builds. Anxiety and fear have nowhere to hide when you take it…

One breath at a time. One move at a time.
One step at a time.

Over the course of the next few weeks, Salma worked on breaking down her new leadership role into smaller steps she could focus on. She knew she needed to instill in her department the feeling that she knew what she was doing and that they would be successful with her leading them. So, she sorted through the stack of projects in her office to find the ones that fit one of two categories. The first category was for the projects that were closest to the finish line and didn't need much time or effort to finish up. The second category was for the most basic and simplistic projects, which would be super easy to knock out quickly.

Salma pulled the team together to talk about the new direction with the projects. The department split up into teams and began knocking out the projects one after another. Every time they completed a project, no matter how small or easy it was, Salma celebrated the win with the department. Now this didn't mean throwing a party for every project, but rather fitting the celebration to the scope of the project. Sometimes it was coffee and bagels for the whole team while other times it was an email congratulating everybody on the completion of the project. She could feel the momentum gaining ground in her department.

And as time wore on, the department got back to the more difficult and time-consuming projects, but everybody was ready because they were confident. She wasn't worried about the end of the long road. She was just deciding on steps to take and then as a team they were taking those steps one at a time. When she had first started her new role and had found herself panicked and running to the bathroom to try to regain her composure, she had felt like Sisyphus from the Greek myth, who had to push the giant boulder up the hill everyday only to have it roll back down again every day. Now she was feeling like the boulder had been pushed over the hill and was hurtling ahead with incredible momentum.

She hadn't found herself in the bathroom freaking out in a long time. In fact, she was even using some of her yoga poses when she felt most stressed out at work. Sometimes when she was sitting at her desk feeling anxious over a deadline, she would stop herself and stand up. Into her Mountain Pose she would go with her shoulders back and feeling the grounded energy coursing through her. Sometimes after a meeting with a client over a new project, she would feel the anxiety kicking in. Immediately she would kick off her shoes and move into Tree Pose with her leg resting on her inner thigh and her arms folded up in front of her. Then the anxiety would calm with every breath she would take, and she would feel balanced and stable in the sea of change.

Salma had even gotten really invested in using the Warrior One Pose when she was struggling with a new idea on a project. When she was blocked from seeing the path out of the issue clearly, she would move into her Warrior One. It didn't matter how she was dressed for the day; she would move her front leg out in front of her. She would twist her back foot to face out and she would slowly bring her arms up over her head and move her body down to a balanced position between her legs. In Warrior One she could feel the power within her growing. She could feel the most creativity and success when she was in this pose. She would stay there until she felt her thoughts singularly focused on the issue at hand. Every time, without fail, a new idea would pop into her head and she would energetically get started on it.

And to think this was all because of the day Salma reluctantly tried the yoga even though she had no interest in it. Since then she had made yoga a regular part of her weekly routine. She was loving yoga. She was loving Lea. Her leadership growth mirrored her yoga growth. It wasn't perfect. It wasn't spectacular. But it was amazing because she was making it happen. And every time she was struggling, she could find Lea right there in her mind telling her to take her life…

One breath at a time. One move at a time.
One step at a time.

The Connection Element

When people called him a millennial, Alden knew they rarely meant it as a positive and endearing term, but he didn't care one bit. No matter what others thought of him, Alden was proud of his millennial ways. Instead of doing everything the way his parents had, and their parents had before them, he did things his own way. He wasn't ever okay with the status quo. He pushed life as much as he could to do his own thing, to find his own way, and to pursue what he loved to do. He wasn't going to just follow everyone else because it was more comfortable. He was going to try new things. It didn't matter if the idea was a little out there. For Alden, that was what being a millennial was all about, and he was proud of it.

Alden was pretty happy with where this mindset had taken his life. He had been a kid who was totally into everything techy. He loved computers and coding, gaming consoles and video games, phones and apps. Anything techy he could get his hands on he was going to get into it and try it. He was constantly playing with tech, learning how it worked, figuring out what he could do with it. He was always trying new ideas and projects that he would see on social media. He was always questioning how and why things worked the way they did. He taught himself everything he could about tech stuff. It was his entire life. It's what he loved.

Alden wasn't into the things that typical kids were supposed to be into (meaning what everyone around him said he should be doing). He wasn't into sports or parties. He wasn't into friends or hanging out. He wasn't into music or books. He wasn't even into school… at least not the boring subjects that didn't help quench his thirst for gadgets and tech stuff. He didn't need to have a group of friends who would keep him away from his tech. The relationships he had with other people took place through a screen, either on his phone or his computer. And this focus on what he loved had paid off.

While struggling through his freshman year of college, Alden developed a super cool app in his Intro to Engineering course. His professor thought it was so great, he even helped Alden connect with a real company to pitch his new app. The company loved the app and wanted to add it to their product line, but Alden didn't want to give away his work to someone else. Instead of selling it and collecting a royalty, Alden set out developing the app himself.

He barely had time for classes at that point, and definitely not time for a social life. He holed himself up on his computer and would go days without interacting with any other human being in real life. He barely found time to even eat, save for a stash of junk food he kept for when he got the munchies. When he did leave his dorm room, he would hear other students snicker at him. He could hear people calling him names such as, "loner," "geek," "loser," and "weird dude." But it didn't faze Alden or his confidence because he had heard it all before. These were the same things they had been saying about him all through his life.

Alden was determined to show all of them that they were wrong. He would show them when he was the next Zuckerberg or Gates or Jobs. Then they would all wish they could be his friend and they would all say how they knew him. The last thing he needed right then in life was friends because that would just take time away from his goals. Plus, he knew he had never really gotten along with other people. He had always struggled connecting with people. It just wasn't his thing. He preferred to interact with people through his tech. That's where he felt most comfortable… always keeping a valley between himself and other people.

At that point in his freshman year of college, Alden's grades were falling apart, and he had zero close friends, but Alden didn't care because everything he did was focused on building and launching the app to the public. Throughout the rest of his freshman year, he worked tirelessly to get the app up and running. One week into his summer, Alden officially launched the app. The launch caught the public like a tornado. Within 24 hours of the launch, the app had been downloaded over 1 million times. It was a huge hit and Alden's phone was ringing off the hook. Everybody wanted to talk to him, interview him, and have him on their talk shows. Kids from his old high school hit him up on Facebook and Instagram trying to connect. It was just as he knew it would be, once he had made it big, then all the ones who had made fun of him would want to be his friend.

Weeks went by as his app continued to set fire to the tech world. He found himself on TV and on podcasts being interviewed. He struggled through it all because he knew he was socially awkward. It wasn't his forte. It wasn't what he enjoyed. What he really wanted to do was to get back to his devices and start building the next viral hit. He preferred the dark and the quiet and the solitude of his own room.

It didn't take long for Alden to figure out that college just wasn't really his thing. When his grades showed up later that summer, he had failed a couple of classes and barely passed his others. He sat down with his parents and told them he was dropping out to start his own tech company based on his first app. They weren't happy, but what could they really say to him? Was college really better than making more money than they had ever seen in their lives? Only a few weeks into his app launch he was already a multi-millionaire. The sky was the limit because he had tons of other ideas to move forward with. Although his parents disagreed and really wanted him to finish school, they came to an impasse that he should take a year off and figure it all out later.

A few years passed by and Alden never returned to college. His startup company had grown big enough that he was no longer running things from a dorm room or from his bedroom at his parents' house. He had even bought himself his own fancy high-rise downtown condo where he could live the cool life with night clubs and bars and restaurants. Not that it really mattered because Alden rarely left his condo, other than to go to his office. He still preferred the tech world over the real world. He had even tried his hand at dating, since he was constantly being asked out by celebrities and famous people, but it just wasn't really his thing. No matter how famous he was, he still saw himself as the geeky, socially awkward, tech nerd.

When things wouldn't go well with friends or dates, Alden would justify it by looking at the number of followers he had on his social media platforms. What did he need from one date or from a group of friends when he had millions of followers on every platform imaginable? He had more friends online than 99.9% of the world, so who cared about what was happening in the real world. Plus, Alden struggled enough trying to connect with the employees in his own company. He had coders and engineers and marketers and public relations people working for him. They all had their roles to fill, but Alden preferred to work on things by himself in his own office. He was at his best with his door closed and nobody around. It was who he was and how he excelled.

It had always been that way. Even all the way back in elementary school, he hated group work. He just wanted to get things done by himself without having to waste all the time talking. He hated when group members would sit around talking while he did all the work. Collaboration sucked for Alden. He was a loner and damn proud of it. And the numbers of followers he had online and the amount of dollars in his bank account proved it was working for him.

There are tons of us who struggle in social settings. It may not be as bad as Alden, but many of us have the same tendencies. It's not that we don't want to be more social, but rather there are so many things that seem to get in the way. Whether it's our busyness, or shyness, or that we have kids that take our time, or we've been burned by friends before, we never seem to forget when these things go wrong for us.

We carry this information and data with us about the past that helps us to make decisions in the present. Take for instance if you were cheated on in a previous relationship. You're going to be hyper-sensitive to any inkling that there is cheating going on in any new relationship. Or, as in the case of Alden, if you've had bad experiences working on group projects in the past, you'll despise group work in the future. It's human nature to use info we've collected from past experiences to help us to deal with new situations.

Imagine the situation where you are raking up leaves in your yard one autumn day. As you reach down to scoop up a part of the pile to put it in the trashcan, you hear the freaky rattling of a rattlesnake tail. You drop the leaves and see a rattlesnake coiled up right near your foot ready to strike. You move away slowly and call an expert to come and remove the snake. Luckily no one was hurt, and you're okay. But think about every time after that for the rest of your life when you go to rake up leaves, you'll be thinking about that rattlesnake. It's part of our nature to store this type of data about the world around us for our basic survival.

Now why are we talking about survival when it comes to our ability to be social beings and find friends? The fact is we are, by nature, tribal beings. This means that we connect with certain people (our tribe) that we know care about us and want to help us in our life. This part of our humanity began thousands of years before as a part of our basic survival needs in that we needed to be surrounded by people that gave us the best chance to survive in a harsh world.

When we fast forward to the current times, we are dealing with the same types of concerns. We establish a feeling about everyone in our social circles in terms of whether they help us to survive (not just physical safety, but if they help us have a better life). For those of us who have been burned too many times by people we thought were on our side, but then turned on us, we are going to struggle to open up. We begin to think everyone is like those who have burned us, and we find aspects of other people that match those who burned us. It can be very difficult to work through, causing us to get stuck in a very limited social circle. We basically shut down before we can be let down or even hurt by others.

As his company continued to expand, Alden was forced to bring on more and more employees because there was more business then he could handle by himself. At the very beginning, he had brought in two of his closest friends, Beckett and Jax, to work with him. They had all been friends since high school, and as he thought about it, they were probably the only two friends he had ever actually had. They were so much like he was, which made Alden comfortable.

There was no pressure to go and do something that Alden didn't want to do because they didn't want to do it either. They all liked the same stuff and doing the same things. It made it easy. No pressure to change. No pressure to get out of their comfort zones. It worked well for the group. Most of the time they hung out, Alden, Beckett, and Jax were all in the same room, but they each were focused on their own screen. A lot of the time they were playing games together through their consoles against teams from all over the world in whatever game was hot at that time. When they all split their ways at college time, they still hung out together in their gaming worlds. It worked well, but it meant Alden became even less connected to anyone outside of that group.

So, when it came time to expand his company, Alden knew that Beckett and Jax were a great pair of guys to turn to for help. They worked closely together, in a very similar fashion to the way they had hung out as teens. They all worked in a garage with computers and tech devices everywhere. Each had their place on a wall of the garage, all facing away from each other. Rarely did they communicate other than to figure out where to grab lunch or dinner. Even figuring that out usually took place through direct messages on their devices.

With all this going on in his life, it should be no surprise that Alden had never really developed any social skills. He rarely ventured out into the real world because it was just not a place where he felt he had ever succeeded. Throughout his life, he had felt like an outsider in just about every social situation, which made it super difficult for him to speak in presentations and meetings. Alden just wanted to work behind the scenes, not out in front of the group. It was one of the reasons he had brought on more people into his company. He knew that he and his coder buddies didn't have that skill set. It wasn't something they wanted to even learn.

So once Alden had the money built up in the company, he hired the top marketers and public relations gurus that he could find. He let them run with the campaigns and sell, sell, sell. It allowed for him to remain in his office and behind his screens doing what he loved to do – develop and create. But while the hiring of new people to handle the things he didn't do well was a blessing, Alden was also finding it was a curse as well. The more people he brought into the company, the more people he was expected to interact with in life. On top of that, no matter how great the people were that he hired, everyone just wanted to hear from the great Alden Lochlan.

At the urging of his board and his closest advisors, Alden would trudge up in front of groups and attempt to talk and answer questions. It wasn't that he was scared to speak, but rather he just didn't know how to connect with people. He could stomach it when it was on national TV or on a podcast or YouTube video because he just had to concentrate on the person right in front of him. The worst moments for Alden were when he had to talk to his staff. These moments made him incredibly sensitive and overly emotional. The slightest bad look or uninterested eyes in the group would send Alden sliding back to middle school and seeing his classmates laughing at him during a presentation. It would set off his emotions and particularly his tears. He would then try to finish talking quickly and get back to his office. He hated these moments. He loathed these moments.

Today was going to be filled with these moments. The company was embarking on a new product that Alden had thought up. His board mandated he bring together a team from within the company to build out the new product. The board had made a point that he could not keep doing things his way, because he was falling behind, and the company numbers were stalling. He had to branch out and allow his team to be a part of the process. Not only would this speed up development, it would free up Alden to keep developing new ideas while working with the team that would take his idea and actually develop it. But the last thing Alden wanted to do was to actually work with others in this process.

Alden walked up to the glass walled meeting room and saw a team of about ten employees sitting at tables inside. He paused for a second at the door before going in. He looked at the group seated inside and found a mix of different members of the staff, including coders, product development staffers, marketers, and a couple of assistants. He took a deep breath as his mind started to race…

> Crap. Why do I have to do this? Why can't I keep doing things the way I always have? This is my company, why can't I do it my way? At least there are a couple of coders in there… I can get along with them. But the rest of them, hopefully they won't look at me. That would be nice. Maybe I can ask them all to look the other way and then I can work with them. Crap. The board won't be happy about that. I have to make it work this time. But this sucks.

As Alden stood outside the door of the meeting room, he kept thinking back to all the sessions he had spent with therapists. As a teenager, Alden's parents had started sending him to regular appointments to try to help him be able to interact better socially with others. He had learned lots of stuff from the therapists he had seen, but they always wanted to go back years and years to try to figure out the root of the problem. He always just wanted to yell to them…

> I already know the root of my problem.… I hate working with other people. It never works. It sucks!!!

But he would sit quietly and talk with the therapists, hoping they would give him some strategies he could actually use to fix the problem. But he always felt it was more of a focus on a diagnosis rather than a fix. As a techy coder, he didn't care about diagnosis, he was constantly seeking new ways to do old things. He was all about fixing the problem rather than sitting around trying to figure it out. With the therapist route not working, he had tried to find something else to help.

In the earliest years of the company, he and Beckett and Jax had been talking about the issues they were all facing, such as meeting new people, and the fact that their bodies were achy from sitting at their computers all day and all night. They started a pact that they would do something physical for at least one hour every day as a group. It would be a forced break to get them up and moving around. They went through several phases, each of which was less successful than the previous one which hadn't been successful either. Let's see… there was the martial arts phase… disaster. There was the gym membership phase… embarrassing. There was the running phase… causing more pain than sitting at the computer. There were the online cardio workouts… a complete mess. Nothing was working. They weren't meeting new people and they weren't getting any relief for their physical issues. They needed something that could help them stretch out their bodies and relax their minds.

It was at that time they stumbled upon yoga. There was a cute little yoga studio right near the gaming shop that they frequented. They kept seeing people going in and out who were smiling and looking happy. So, on a whim one day, they went inside. After meeting the girl at the front desk, she invited them to try out a class and see what they thought. The first class didn't solve all their issues in life, far from it, but they did leave there smiling. Their bodies felt good and their minds actually felt relatively clear. Plus, there were tons of interesting and attractive people in the room, not that the three coders had the guts to talk to any of them. But they made a pact to keep coming for a yoga session every other day as a break from their work. Over time, they began to love the sessions. It was the only thing they all loved that had absolutely no tech involved at all. That was truly amazing!

As the years went on, they still struggled to actually talk to anyone in the class, except for one person, the instructor, a great lady named Lea. Alden wished that everyone he worked with was a clone of Lea. She was one of the few people ever in his life that he actually enjoyed interacting with. It was always so easy to talk to her. She would listen to him and the best part was that he never ever felt judged by her. He had felt judged by everyone for so long that he had grown accustomed to expecting it from everybody he interacted with. But Lea was different. She cared for Alden. She never made him feel awkward or geeky or like a loner. She was so welcoming and sweet. So, he kept coming back.

Alden pulled himself out of his memories and began to open the door to the meeting, but he couldn't stop thinking about his yoga and something that Lea had said that had stuck with him for a long time. He had told Lea how much he enjoyed the yoga and the fact that he didn't feel awkward in the classes. He had shared with her how much he struggled when working with other people and how bad he felt about it constantly. As he told her, he half expected her to come down on his issues, just as so many people – parents, teachers, board members, employees – had always done to him. They made him feel terrible about it.

But Lea's response was different. She had said to him, "We all have areas of growth in our lives. It is not a weak point, but rather an opportunity for change. How boring would life be if we were perfect and never had anything to work on and improve in our lives? I love to find my areas of growth and focus intently on them. They are different for everybody, but the path is similar. Think of yourself as the caterpillar. You want to become a butterfly, but you are stuck. Don't stop trying and be okay with life as a caterpillar. Don't be afraid to change the existence that you know, because what waits on the other side could be a beautiful spectacle."

Alden snapped back from his memory and looked inside the room. Everybody was turned and looking at him as he stood at the door. He became self-conscious immediately. They must be thinking he's nuts just standing there unable to come in. But then he smiled as he thought of the conversation with Lea again. He took his hand off the door handle and immediately turned and walked back towards his office. He heard Beckett call to him, "What are you doing Alden? Didn't the board say you had to make it work this time? Come on man, you can do it. I know you can."

Alden smiled as he nodded his head, "Thanks Beck. You're right. I'm not running away from it. But I just thought of something I absolutely need to do before I go in there. Can you go tell them I forgot something and that I'll be right back?" As Becket went over to the meeting room to talk to them, Alden slipped into his own office and closed the door behind him. He walked over to his desk and opened his big main drawer. Inside he found a series of post-it notes that he had written for himself such as passwords or motivational quotes. He searched through and found the one he needed. On the paper was a quote that Lea had shared with him about working with others. It was just what he needed to go into that meeting. He left the office and walked back down to the meeting room. He took a seat at the table and put the note down right in front of his device so only he could see it. He looked down at it again and smiled...

**Break down my walls and
build bridges to others around me.**

Experts on human development suggest that humans develop in their lives through interactions with an ever-expanding world that brings in new information and data. Think about the ever-growing social circles that you've experienced in your life. As a small child it's just your immediate family around you, but then you go to school and there are other kids, teachers, and parents of your friends. Then you start playing sports or join a club and you meet kids from other schools. Then you go to work or college and have all these new people and places to deal with. In each step, your social circle is expanding.

With each step, we interact with new people, ideas, thoughts, situations, relationships, and problems. The quality (or lack thereof) and the success (or lack thereof) of the interactions impacts our development either positively or negatively. If we struggle with a particular interaction in our life, then we are going to get stuck dealing with that same issue over and over again until we can resolve it and move on. It's like a *sticky spider web* and we're the fly stuck in it who can't escape.

Just like Alden, we all have particularly sticky spider web aspects of our lives where we struggle with certain issues. For Alden, his sticky spider web is trying to collaborate or work with others. His problem goes all the way back to 3rd grade when his friend Eric showed up at his house for a school project where they had to build a model of Abe

Lincoln's log cabin. But Eric came with a bunch of toys and games to play with while Alden was all set up with the materials needed for the project. The afternoon went as you can imagine, Eric played with toys while Alden worked on the project. It was the beginning of a sticky social web for Alden. One that he would never really recover from, because every group project he faced after that, he had the memory of this earliest interaction warning him to watch out for group work. Add 20+ years of situations that always seemed to go the same way as the first (maybe without the toys) and you can see how Alden is the way that he is.

We all have sticky spider webs in our lives. It may not be collaboration like it is for Alden, but maybe it's relationships (especially if our parents got divorced), or it's with school (if we got low grades early on) or it's with driving a car (if we got in a bad accident as a new driver), or it's asking for help (if we were made to feel weak or stupid when we asked for help). There are myriad parts of our lives that can get sticky.

Particularly when we are in the role of a leader, our sticky points and issues seem to always be seated right next to us. Often as followers, we can hide our issues and just get by with covering them up, so no one notices. We can focus in on what we do well and what we excel at and let others do the parts that we don't like to do or cause issues for us. But as leaders, it is hard to hide some of this. It is possible, but like Lea's metaphor of the caterpillar and the butterfly, often our leadership capabilities will remain within the cocoon until we are able to change ourselves. It is not always an easy process, but it is needed for our leadership to be effective.

As leaders, we are a focal point for followers and employees. They are watching us and noticing us and studying us. This can cause a lot of pressure to build up on our shoulders. It can make us self-conscious. It can wreak havoc on our psyche. We get caught up in worrying about what others think of us. This is never more integral to our leadership then when we are working in groups. We're surrounded by others in a group process, so we feel like we are on display all the time. We don't worry about the group members seeing our positives. It's as though the great things about us are a given, like everybody already knows they exist. What we get caught up on in group settings are our insecurities, our struggles, and our issues. We worry that the closer we work with others the more apt they are to see through us, and the more able they'll be to see what we're trying to hide.

This isn't about some hidden nefarious secret as though we're a movie super villain hiding our identity from the unsuspecting public. It's about the fact that we keep things about ourselves hidden from those around us because we're afraid we'll be judged. It's all about insecurity. For example, maybe it's that we don't process new info as fast as others around us, or we don't know the technology as well as our colleagues, or we think we don't have enough experience to be on the team, or our clothes aren't as nice as our peers. Our weaknesses. Our fears. Our insecurities. Think about how you deal with these items in your life. How big is the circle of people who you've actually shared your insecurities with? Maybe your immediate family knows some of them? Maybe a couple of your closest besties? Probably a loved one, but this group is very small and so we hide and cover our weaknesses and hope everybody moves on.

We can hide them easier as a member of the team because we can just melt into the huddled masses. But put us in a leadership role and uh oh... we're on display. Insecurities are one of the biggest reasons why people don't like to work in collective groups. The question is, how do we put these insecurities to the side so we can do great collective work? Leadership is group work, so we have to figure out how to connect with others in meaningful ways. It seems that Alden has to figure this out before his project fizzles out...

Alden looked down at his post-it note one more time and took a big breath. He looked up to find everybody staring right at him. It was as though they all had Superman's X-ray vision and could see right through him. What would they find? A guy who struggles to work with others in groups. A guy who has done cool things but might have run out of great ideas. A guy who spent his entire life holed up in his room on his devices. Yeah, that was the one that was the scariest. What if they figured out he wasn't who he appeared to be? What if they figured out that no matter how many followers he had, how many interviews he did… that he was by nature… just a socially awkward kid pretending to be a functioning adult. He looked down at the note and read the words again… Break down my walls and build bridges to others around me. He breathed in and out again…

> You can do this Alden. You know what you are doing. You are the CEO. You are the leader. They want to work with you. They want to be on your team. Don't believe it… then ask them. Why are they here?

He looked at the group again and asked everyone if they could introduce themselves and share why they were on this new development team. As they took their turns speaking out, the answers surprised Alden. Not one person showed any inclination that they had been forced to join the team. All of them shared how they had joined the company because they wanted to work with and learn from Alden Lochlan. He was shocked, but doubt was there as well…

> Hey buddy… over here… remember us… yeah couldn't they just be buttering you up… kissing up

to you because you're the boss. They're probably
forced to be on this team and can't wait to get off it.

One of the more senior members of the organization,
Kelsie, who had been with Alden and the company for a
long time, spoke up for the group as though she could read
Alden's thoughts, "Everybody who is here asked to join this
team. The list of names who wanted to be on this team was
huge, but each department worked to find the right people
to be a part of this." Alden looked at her inquisitively and
responded with a question, "What's so big about this?"
Kelsie started laughing then quickly stopped when she
realized that Alden wasn't joking. "Oh, you're seriously
asking that?" Alden nodded his head and shrugged his
shoulders. Kelsie continued on, "Oh, well as you know this
is really the first time you have actually led a real team here
in the company, so everyone wanted to work with you rather
than just work *for* you. They think it's an honor to work with
you on this project. That's why they're excited."

Alden turned and walked over to one of the windows that
looked out over the downtown skyline. The rest of the team
started looking at each other trying to figure out what was
going on. Alden couldn't believe that this was the first time
he had ever done this. He knew he hated group work, but
seriously had he never run a developmental team at the
company? That was crazy. As he looked out the window, he

realized that his normal excuses for not being a part of a group had been thrown out the window. These people actually wanted to be in his group. They were ready to work… not just play. He turned and peeked back at the group… he was right, nobody had brought their toys to the meeting like his friend Eric had back in 3rd grade. They wanted to work. He looked back out the window…

> How do I start working with them? I want to break my wall. I want to build a bridge. But I don't really know what to do. The worst thing I could do is to stand looking out this window like a moron. Talk about socially awkward. If I'm not careful, when I turn back around, they'll all be gone. Lea always talked about taking things in life one step at a time. About not trying to do everything at once, but to try to take one step. Just one step. Just one tiny connection. Maybe I just need to be vulnerable…

He turned back around and walked towards the table as he opened up to the group as best as he could, "Thank you all for being here and wanting to be a part of this. It means a lot. It's really hard for me to work with others. I've gotten used to working by myself. So, it's not that I dislike any of you… it's just that I'm super uncomfortable. So hopefully you'll all understand and know that I am probably going to screw this up… but you have my word I'm going to try my best to work it out. I know I'll make mistakes, but I hope you'll stick with me as I try this all out for the first time."

He looked straight down at his spot at the table. His post-it note shined under the light… *Break down my walls and build bridges to others around me.* He thought to himself that he may not have broken down the wall in only a few words, but he had at least taken a sledgehammer out and tried to put a dent in it. It was going to take a lot more swings, but he never backed down from hard work, so why not try it. He was trying his best Chip Gaines and Shorty impersonation, because he was feeling like this was *demo day*. Time to bust up some walls that had been around way too long. As he looked up, Alden saw everybody at the table smiling and nodding. One young man spoke up, "We're totally with you. Just lead the way and we'll follow." Alden smiled knowing he had made his first dent in that stupid wall he had built.

What Alden is dealing with throughout this story is that his **Connection Element of Leadership** is blocked. Just because this one element is blocked, it doesn't mean he's not being an effective leader. His profitability and innovation and following on social media shows that he is leading people from all over the world. But in this one specific element of leadership – his ability to connect with others – he is struggling. It's been a long and arduous struggle for him going back into the furthest reaches of his own childhood. But by struggling in this one area, it's sharpened his skills in other areas. It's like the stories we hear about people who lose one of their senses (e.g., sight, sound) and by losing this sense, they are forced to be incredible in their other senses.

One can find that with leaders in particular, if they struggle in one element of their leadership, they typically excel in other areas. In Alden's case, his inability to work with others has forced him to learn how to do things on his own. This has brought him incredible success because he has used his weakness as a driver for other aspects of his life. Rare are the leaders who are strong in every aspect of their leadership.

All leaders have a set of skills, capacities, and knowledge they use to lead others. There are some aspects they excel in, some that they do well in, some they do okay in, and some they totally struggle in. This is common. This is regular. This is okay. Did you hear that? You can be a leader, even if you don't have every skill you think a leader needs. As long as you are able to use the skills, capacities, and knowledge that you do have, you can lead others. By strengthening the aspects of our leadership that we're good at, we're able to often cover up our weaker elements. But one of the keys to a great leader is their ability to be real and vulnerable. Alden is experiencing that right here. Instead of hiding his weakness and trying to act like it's all good, nothing to see here… he's admitting to his team that he struggles at something. This might seem strange, but it is so important.

The key to vulnerability is that you're being honest with your followers. You're not trying to act perfect, but rather you're being straight up with everybody. You're getting out in front of potential issues by saying, "I struggle with this, but I'm working on it." Now the next step is to actually try to work on it as your words can't be *fake news*. But as a leader who shows their vulnerability, you're actually going to build more followers. This seems backwards to the way that we think of leaders, but it's true. If we try to be perfect in front of our followers, they're going to eventually figure out our flaws and they'll leave because if the leader can't be honest about that, then how can the leader be trusted on other stuff.

Now some of you might read this and think, "So as a leader I need to tell everybody about all of my flaws and issues and struggles. What do you want me to do, carry a sheet of paper around that I hand out to everyone about all the issues that I have in life? You want me to wear a scarlet letter to let everyone know what's wrong with me?" No way. That isn't what this is about. You don't have to share everything with everybody. It's more about not trying to fake it till you make it. It is about being real and authentic and trustworthy. They don't have to know everything you struggle with, but they have to know that you're a real person, just like they are.

The other aspect that followers love about vulnerability, is the way in which they can get actively involved in filling in that gap for their leader. If they can take on the task that is difficult for the leader, then the follower feels empowered and here is the little secret… the followers begin to develop their own leadership which only makes your team stronger.

Alden made it through the first meeting with the new team. It didn't go perfectly smooth, but he made it through without getting overly emotional. Anytime he perceived that someone didn't like what he was saying, he would look down at his post-it note mantra. It would kickstart him back on the path to trying to break down his walls. Once the meeting had ended and he was back in the safety and security of his own office, he sat at his desk for a while and just tuned out. He sat meditating in Easy Pose in his chair. He needed to calm the anxiety that had built up inside him during the meeting.

The group had left it that they would meet every day to check in on progress and go through various aspects of the new product. It was going to be a tough few months for Alden, especially since he was going to have to actually give away parts of the process to members of the team that he normally just cranked out on his own. But he knew that by getting uncomfortable, eventually it would help him to do that more often in the future. He knew he had to do that in order to keep the board backing him.

Knowing that he was going to really test his ability to connect with others, Alden knew he needed to beef up the one aspect of his life that could help him with this… his yoga. He was a regular in yoga classes, but he was going to need to focus on his ability to break down his walls and replace them with bridges. Later that day he found himself again in the comfort of Lea's Life Studio, the only place where he could truly be free from his life. He always made it a point to leave his phone and devices either in his car or back at his condo. He wanted to unplug from the world and focus only on himself when he was at the studio.

As Alden walked in, he found Lea bumping around putting things together for the session. He bounded right over to her, as she was one of the few people in the world that he felt at total peace in her presence. "Lea you would have been totally proud of me today!" Lea giggled at the words, "Oh Alden, I am always proud of you." Alden smiled and gave her a hug. "No, seriously Lea, this time I really mean it. I actually used one of your mantras to get me through a very difficult time. And it worked. Seriously it worked so well."

Lea smiled at the young man. "I bet it had something to do with working with other people, huh?" Alden shook his head in disbelief… how did she always know exactly what he was talking about? Alden went on to tell her all about how he used the mantra to center himself when he was feeling anxious and uncomfortable. He told Lea that the best part of it all was that he had put a hole in his wall. Lea smiled with pride to hear Alden working through his struggles. She said to him, "That settles it. I had been trying to figure out our focus for today's session. And the universe is speaking to me through you. Can you write that mantra you used up on the board? And wait until I show you some really powerful poses that can make that mantra come to life."

The session was just what he needed to prepare for the work that lay ahead of him. It wasn't the actual development work... he could do that with his eyes closed and his hands tied behind his back. No, the real work was going to be collaborating. Lea introduced three different poses to the class that day – Cat-Cow Pose, Wide Legged Seated Forward Bend, and the Superman Pose – that aligned most with what Alden needed. In those poses he found his mind thinking about breaking down the walls as he breathed in. When he exhaled, he thought only of building the bridges he needed. He felt strong and confident as he worked in the poses. As he left the studio that night, he promised himself he would make sure he did a shortened yoga routine every morning that included the three poses. He knew this would get his mind and body in the right place for collaboration.

Now the collaboration process moving forward wasn't some fairy tale miracle by any means. The Fairy Godmother didn't wave her wand, and everything went perfectly. There were some definite downs along the way, but there were also plenty of ups as well. Alden failed several times at connecting with the team. One time in particular stood out. The team had been slogging through some heavy work for several days in a row and he knew everyone was tired and not thinking clearly. People were short with each other and there were tons of arguments over details. Alden knew he had to do something to fix the situation. He found some ideas on the internet and planned to have a lunch outside followed by a game of old school foursquare. He even went out and taped off a court in the parking lot outside the building for the game. He ordered sandwiches from some fancy little sub shop down the street. The plan was great. The idea was great. The goal was perfect for connecting everybody again.

But even the best plans don't always go quite right. It ended up that the sandwich order was a disaster. Basically, every person in the group couldn't eat some part of the sandwich. For some it was an allergy to the bread or the tomatoes or the veggies. Some didn't eat meat. Others were lactose intolerant and couldn't eat the cheese. At the end of the meal, there was a giant pile of leftover sandwich parts which people couldn't eat. The problem was that Alden was new to the social life. He had never really hung out with anyone socially, so he had no idea how many different dietary needs there were. But it actually helped him and the others to connect as they laughed heartily at Alden's lack of understanding of the diverse needs of the team.

The foursquare game was even more of a disaster. This team was not exactly the most athletic group of people assembled. Rallies were short or even completely non-existent. People fell down. They swung at the ball and completely whiffed. It culminated in Alden getting hit square in the face by a winning point, sending him sprawling out onto the parking lot blacktop. But despite the farce of an activity that it was, everybody laughed and had a good time. Alden's doubts and insecurities kept coming out throughout the lunch and game. He knew he had made mistakes, mistakes that other people who were at least socially competent, would not have made. But as the group went walking back into the building, Kelsie walked up beside Alden. She leaned in and whispered, "That was absolutely perfect. It's exactly what we all needed. You did a great job connecting us as a team again."

Alden smiled to himself realizing that he didn't have to be perfect to build that bridge to others. He just had to get out there and try. And it had brought the team together as they started absolutely rolling after that point. As the weeks progressed, Alden found himself rarely looking down at his mantra post-it. For the first time in his life he was actually building relationships with other people. He had even gotten to the point that despite these people being his employees, he was actually starting to see them as friends. It was a big step in his growth not only as a leader, but as a living breathing human being. The walls were coming down and the bridges were being built one day at a time.

The Connection Element of Leadership is all about a leader's ability to build relationships with others. Leadership cannot exist within a vacuum. It doesn't exist in only a single leader. Leading is about motivating other people to move towards a vision of change. There are no leaders without followers, just as there are no followers without leaders. The key to leadership is the relationship between leader and follower. It's all about collaboration and group work. This is what the Connection Element of Leadership is all about. But followers do not just follow blindly in most cases, they follow leaders who they connect with and believe in.

Trust and relationship-building are the central tenants that run deep through the Connection Element of Leadership. It is what the second chakra, known as the water or sacral chakra, is all about. The chakra focuses on our emotional well-being and feelings, our sexuality and relationships, as well as our life energy. When this element is in balance, the leader is not standing out in front of the group telling everyone where to go and what to do. That is more of a management style (and yes at times leaders need to do this). But in the Connection Element, the leader is a part of the group. They are participating with the followers. They are building relationships with the followers.

Everyone, including the leader and the followers, have to feel as though they are a part of the team. It's the old adage of everyone rowing the boat in the same direction. But in this Element, the leader is not standing up on the deck steering or barking out the rhythm. They are seated at an oar with their followers. They are rowing. They are working. They are a part of the team. To do this, the leader is humble and comfortable enough to be with their followers.

The Connection Element of Leadership is one of the most powerful methods of leading in that it does an incredible job of building other leaders from within the group. All members of the collective have a voice in what is happening and what is being done. Everyone has a voice in the decision-making process. Now you might think there are some real issues with this notion of everyone at the table having a voice. This is true. Sometimes when everyone has a voice, nothing gets done because no one makes a final decision. Or even worse, a bad idea gets promoted because everyone in the group is afraid to step up and say there is something wrong. That is where the actual leader comes in. At times they must energize their Element and take on the leadership. But they can do this at any time, because they have built trust with their followers. When they have to step up and take the proverbial *bull by the horns,* they can do it.

While there might be some drawbacks such as group think and a lack of decision-making in this element of leadership, the positives far outweigh the negatives. This is because when followers feel they are an active part of the team and that their voice gets heard, they are more motivated to be a part of the team. Few people want to just be constantly told what to do. They want to feel like they have a voice. This is where leaders who have an energized Connection Element of Leadership excel. By building relationships, they are empowering the collective team to do great things.

And in this case, despite the fact that Alden had always struggled to connect with other people, he is an example that we all can change who we are and what we are good at. It takes time. It takes hard work. It takes dedication. There are going to be setbacks like catching a foursquare ball right between the eyes. But in the end, the Connection Element Leader is someone that people want to work with. And the impact on the team and the leader can be amazing, as we have a feeling Alden is about to figure out for himself...

Over the course of the next few months, Alden and his team had made huge strides. Whereas Alden had been filled with apprehension and anxiety at the thought of working in teams, he was actually enjoying himself. Work was more fun than it had ever been. He had found himself many times in his office with other members of the staff sitting and talking. And it wasn't work related. They were talking about the latest movies, or their family lives, their hobbies, and all the other stuff that Alden had basically shut out of his life.

Alden had even started a Social Hour Team within the company. He had asked for volunteers who wanted to lead an hour every week where everyone stopped their work and got together to do something social. Sometimes it was a game they all played. Sometimes it was just a snack and drink time. Sometimes it was a movie day. But every week, no matter what they had on their plates in terms of projects, everybody stopped and spent time with each other. It was like a whole new world. Alden found himself actually enjoying most of it. Yeah, most of it. There were times where he still struggled with the whole social life and locked himself up in his office... so he wasn't bothered. And there was nothing wrong with that because there were times where that was needed. But he was making big strides.

The success of the first work team that he had led, had sparked him to build in more group projects, something he thought he would never ever do in his life. He had come to the realization that his own lack of working with others was rubbing off on the environment at work. And through his experiences with the first group project, his eyes had been opened to the notion that he wanted the environment to be more open and social and friendly, and most importantly, collaborative. They were all in pursuit of the same goals, so why not be stronger as a team than a bunch of individuals. But he had to set the example. He had to get through his issues. He had to knock down the walls and build bridges.

And it wasn't just in the workplace where he was making changes. He was becoming more comfortable in who he was. He found himself at times just walking through the city's downtown taking in the people and life outside his condo. Even in the yoga studio he was different. Whereas before he always tried to find the same corner of the room where he was the most isolated, he had begun to move around a little more. He tried his best to introduce himself to other people. And one time he even finally put his mat down next to a woman he had seen in the classes for many years but had never had the guts to talk to. He set up next to her for several sessions in a row. Each session he took things one step further. The first time he didn't even look at her. The next time he looked at her and smiled when she smiled at him. After several sessions, he actually even said hello and started talking with her. It wasn't some romantic comedy where everything worked out the first day, but he was slowly breaking down the old wall and building a new bridge.

A few months later, he found himself again at the door of the meeting room. Inside the room was his team. He thought back to that first time he tried to go in that door. He remembered how they were all sitting orderly in their spots around the table and the room was completely silent. He remembered the stress he felt. He remembered the fear that had frozen him. He remembered the feeling of wanting to go back to his office and hide. He started to laugh thinking about the note that contained the mantra from Lea's class about breaking down the walls and building the bridges. He no longer carried that post-it with him because he no longer needed it. He was a team player. He was a collaborator.

He still ultimately loved working by himself. That was never going to change because that was where he did his best work. But he was now comfortable working with others. And he had seen the positive impact of the group process. It was obvious as he looked into the room. Instead of all sitting quietly in their seats, small groups were moving about talking excitedly, sharing stories, and laughing with each other. It was a sight that would make any leader proud.

The best part of the meeting on this day was that it was all about success and the final preparations for their launch.

The group project had worked beautifully. That night was the official launch of the product the first team he had worked with had built out. They had rented out a ballroom in a downtown hotel and had marketed the launch everywhere. Whereas with Alden's earliest launches that were quiet and personal, this was all about connecting with the world. News media were going to be there, talk show hosts, celebrities, social media influencers, everybody. It was going to be super cool, even for Alden. He was actually excited (and very nervous too) to be a part of it. The team went through the launch details and then left for the day.

That night at the launch when Alden's limo pulled up, he could see the mass of people standing outside the hotel. A red carpet was rolled out the door to where the cars were pulling up. Alden looked out the tinted windows and saw Beckett and Jax standing with his own parents waiting so they could all go in together. For a moment, Alden felt a pit in his stomach…

> There you are anxiety. I knew you'd show up tonight. I know you want me to get back to that garage and bury myself in my tech. But I have bad news for you tonight. You don't have any walls to hide behind inside me. The walls are gone. All you'll find are bridges. Bridges to my friends. To my family. To my team. And even a very special bridge I built recently. So, get lost anxiety. You aren't welcome anymore.

Alden reached into his pocket and pulled out a little yellow post-it that was, at this point, pretty crumpled up. But the words on the note were as clear as day... *Break down my walls and build bridges to others around me.* He smiled as he read it, then tucked it away and stepped out of the limo. Beckett and Jax and his parents walked down to greet him. He waved and said hello, but then he turned around and leaned down into the limo and extended his hand.

A hand grabbed hold of his and then a young woman stepped out of the limo. To the shock of all standing there, Alden hugged and then passionately kissed the woman. He took hold of her hand and they turned to face the crowd. Beckett and Jax stood in shock, they couldn't remember if they had ever seen him with a date. Alden said proudly, "I'd like to introduce you to my girlfriend. Her name is Tallulah. We met in a yoga class."

**Break down my walls and
build bridges to others around me.**

The Action Element

Taylor always loved the feeling of sitting on her mat waiting for her yoga session to begin. No matter how busy her life was, she found her cross-legged meditation pose to be peaceful, relaxing, and calm. She didn't care what was happening around her as she focused on feeling her hips connecting to the floor. She didn't think about all the to-dos on her list as she crossed her legs and tucked her feet in under her knees. All the worries in her mind would go away when she would tip her head back and lengthen her spine out. It felt calm. It felt relaxing. It felt good.

Taylor knew that outside of her yoga practice, this feeling was rare and fleeting in her life. Off the mat and outside the yoga studio, her world seemed to exist inside a washing machine set to the fastest spin cycle it could handle. Her calmness and the ability to open her mind during yoga is what kept her coming back to Lea's Life Studio week after week. She needed the time on the mat. She found good luck with doing yoga at home as well, but it was never quite the same as being in the studio. There she could actually escape the busyness of life. She could check into total Zen mode.

Her life hadn't always been that busy, but lately it just seemed to never slow down. She was always moving and working, but she felt like she was never really going anywhere. It was that feeling of being inside the washing machine just spinning around rapidly in circles over and over and over again. The spin was so fast that Taylor couldn't even figure out how to slow it down or stop it. So, spin and spin and spin she did over and over and over again. Rinse, soak, spin, repeat. Rinse, soak, spin, repeat. Rinse, soak, spin, repeat. That was the life of an emerging entrepreneur.

As she sat meditating in Easy Pose, she heard Lea's voice at the front of the room. The session was ready to begin. Taylor's face brightened with a big smile because she was excited. She loved yoga and had been doing it for years. She first tried it out as a high school track and field athlete. Her coaches had sent the team to yoga to help them with their breathing, balance, strength, focus, relaxation, and recovery. The coaches felt it was a great break from their running practice and it offered the opportunity to work their minds and bodies in a different way. Taylor had loved the feeling so much that she continued to do yoga as her track career continued into college.

As Lea started the group on the sequence, Taylor effortlessly worked through the routine. She felt confident. She felt powerful. She felt in control. If only she could feel that same confidence, power, and control off the mat as well. Her decisiveness on the mat was equally matched by her passivity off the mat. She felt as though she would be so much more successful if she could live her entire life on a mat. It was a funny thought, because she actually spent most of her time on an exercise mat now that she was a couple of years into her own new online business which focused on health and fitness. She had left her corporate job to try a new path, a path that made her feel good at first. She did it to be her own woman. To be her own boss. To live the life she wanted to live. She had believed in it so much at that point because she knew she was damn good at the health and fitness stuff. It was what she had done her entire life.

Whether she was leading an exercise class or making a video for her clients, Taylor was what she needed to be. But get her off that mat, and it was a whole other story. When it came to all the other aspects of her business, she usually felt lost, unable to decide on what to do, always questioning herself and her decisions. Taylor took a deep breath as she rotated her arms to move into the next step of Warrior Pose. Ah, now this felt good. This felt strong. This felt powerful. She caught herself continuing to think about her business which she didn't want to do during her yoga...

> Stop thinking about life. Stop thinking about the business. Stop thinking outside the room. Focus on here and now. Focus on the move. Take a breath. I can worry about all that other stuff later. Right now, it's yoga. It's what I do well. It's what I enjoy.

Lea told the class that she wanted them to do their last sequence on their own pace and to select the poses that spoke most to them and their lives in that moment. Taylor knew exactly what was calling to her… her solar plexus and the fire chakra. She lowered her stomach down to the ground and arched up into Cobra Pose. She could feel her chest tighten and flex. This felt good. She stretched her legs out and moved them behind her. She arched her back up and lowered her chin towards the ground. There it was, a beautiful Downward Dog. She loved her yoga. She loved this feeling. She slowly brought her head back down to the ground. It was time for the Plank Pose. Taylor pushed herself up onto her forearms and focused herself on holding her body in a perfect straight line…

> You can do this T. You're strong. You're powerful. You're confident. You believe in you. You're living the life you want to live. You're doing what you want to do. You're the woman. Take control. Take the power. Take action. Make it happen girl.

Taylor held her plank tight. She could feel the power coursing through her chest like a fire had been lit. It felt so good to feel this way. There were times in her business where she felt this way, but too many times it felt like her chest was caving in under the pressure. On the mat, she felt like Atlas holding the earth on her shoulders. Off the mat, it felt like the earth was flattening her like a pancake.

Our lives exist on a sliding spectrum of confidence, ranging from total confidence to a complete lack of confidence. It's a sliding spectrum because we aren't in one single place all the time in every aspect of our lives. Some things we feel great about, others not so much. Most of us are just like the Two-Face character from the Batman comics. No, not the villainy aspect of this character where we have a split personality with an evil side... but rather we have a face of confidence and a face of no confidence. Take Taylor for example. She is super confident on an exercise mat but lacks the confidence on the business side of her company. She is great and strong and powerful when she is doing that which she knows she is really good at – athletics, exercise, yoga, running. But put the most basic business concept in front of her and Taylor would probably cower in the corner hoping it would pass her by in the night.

It's all about which face we are showing the world... the confident one or the not-confident one. This can be found in all walks of life, not just in business. Think of the star high school volleyball player who is ready for anything the game throws her way on the court, but when she gets into her math class, she loses all that confidence and just watches the clock waiting for the class to end. Or take the dad who runs his business super successfully. He can step up in front of any group and speak to them with confidence and power. But get him home in front of his teenage son and you could hear a pin drop. What the hell does he talk to the kid about? He tells himself he doesn't understand his son anymore, that teenage life is difficult, and he should just stay out of the way. Or take the schoolteacher who loves working with her students and is so connected with each of them. She builds super strong bonds with her kids that help them to succeed. But when it comes to talking to their parents at conferences or on the phone, she goes frozen and afraid to speak.

Our two faces of confidence come in many different forms, totally dependent on us as humans. Think to yourself about the things about you that you feel strong about. Got 'em? You probably feel really good right now. You feel strong. You feel empowered. You're ready to take the world on. Now think about the parts of your life where you think you fail or struggle. Got 'em? Now you probably don't feel so good. The smile is gone. You feel afraid or weak. You want to hide them from the world. The way in which we see our confidence is based on the feedback we have received from the world throughout our lives. Get positive feedback for something you do well, and you're going to grow confidence in that area. But get negative feedback or get made fun of for something and you're going to stop believing in that area completely. The feedback from the world sets our beliefs about ourselves, which then controls how we will experience these things in the future.

Imagine the child who goes up to give a presentation in her classroom and messes it up. Classmates are laughing at her. The teacher points out all the things she did wrong. She gets a low grade on the presentation. You think she is going to have a lot of confidence the next time she goes to do a presentation? She will go in thinking she is going to screw up again. And when she messes something up, she will only get more feedback that says, "You suck at this." Speaking in front of others quickly becomes a massive avalanche that is hurtling down the mountain gathering more girth until it's so massive it crushes her. And guess what, her confidence is nowhere to be found having run off the mountain long before it can be crushed too!

Think about Taylor. She has been a top athlete, even competing collegiately. When she faces athletic stuff, she believes totally in her abilities. But her business has been a struggle (as it is for every start-up company), so she lacks the confidence because she is waiting for the next thing to go wrong (because it always seems to go wrong). It may seem a dire situation... like why even try if it's not going to work? But never fear, because there is good news. Our brains have neuroplasticity, which means they are able to adapt and change all throughout life. It means we don't have to give up and wait for the massive avalanche to crush us. We can see our lives differently. We can take action to change our lives.

As the session came to an end, Taylor was rolling up her mat and collecting her stuff. Lea came by and gave Taylor a big hug. "It's so great to see you again, T. You looked strong today!" Taylor smiled at the kind words. This is one of the reasons why she loved coming to Lea's sessions. Lea always knew how to make Taylor feel so confident. It was something Taylor needed more of outside of the studio...

If only I could clone Lea and have her sit with me at home as I try to run my business... then I'd succeed.

"How is the business going?" Lea asked inquisitively. "It's going. It's moving. It's coming along," Taylor responded as she forced a halfhearted smile. It was a trick she had been doing for a while whenever people asked about her business. She didn't want anyone to know she was struggling. That running the business was super difficult. She didn't want anyone to know she wasn't sure she could actually make it.

She didn't want anyone to think she was weak or a failure. So, she faked the smile and said it was all good and it was coming along. It always seemed to throw people off the scent, and they'd move on with the conversation, but Taylor knew it wasn't going to fool Lea, because nothing ever did.

"That reminds me of me when I first started this studio many years ago. I talked the same way as you are. I tried to hide from everyone around me that I was afraid. You know the old saying... fake it till you make it... that was me for sure. I thought of quitting so many times. I thought it might be easier to just go work for somebody else again." Taylor nodded in agreement as Lea continued, "But the problem was I was talking down to myself and saying I couldn't hack it. But at a certain point, I realized I was the only person saying this. Everyone around me believed in me. They all told me how they wished they could do what I was doing. They all wished they could have the guts I had. And yet, I didn't feel like I had anything they were telling me I had."

Taylor started laughing, "Do you have a bug in my house? Are you hearing every conversation I have with myself? Because you're saying everything I've been saying." Lea started laughing, "Don't worry, I'm not big brother listening in on you. I just know from experience. And guess what, it's not just you and me who go through this. It's everybody who tries to do something different. Whether it's business, or health, or family… any change brings out our duality. Our dual sides begin fighting with each other. It's like the old angel or devil on your shoulder. One side saying you're the greatest, the other saying you're the worst. It's the dark and light, sun and moon, yin and yang. I won when I stopped listening to the side that was telling me I couldn't do it."

Taylor nodded in agreement, "That's what I need outside this studio. I need to figure out how to believe the way I used to in my skills and abilities…" Lea cut in before she could finish, "You are saying it wrong." Taylor cocked her head not understanding what Lea meant. The old yogi continued on, "It's not about *used to* and now you don't. You do believe in your own skills and abilities. You do know how great you are. You just don't believe the things you are great at can help in the areas you're struggling in. But they do. Think of it like wearing a tool belt with all the skills and abilities you have developed. Now you just have to figure out how to use those tools to fix the problems in your business world."

Taylor's head was spinning with thoughts. She hadn't ever thought about life that way. She reached out and hugged Lea. "I know I tell you this all the time Lea, but you're the absolute best. I wish you could live in my house and be there as I struggle." Lea began to laugh and shake her head. "You don't need me T. All you need is yourself. All you need is to listen to the side that is saying you can do it. All you need to do is repeat this mantra to yourself and not just in your mind, but actually say the words out loud… I am strong. I am powerful. I am confident. I believe in myself."

Taylor looked down at the ground sheepishly. Lea pushed on, "Go ahead and try it. Right now. Speak to yourself. Empower yourself." Taylor looked up at Lea and repeated, "I am strong. I am powerful. I am confident. I believe in myself." She repeated it again and again. Each time she said the mantra she could feel her shoulders rolling back and her spine extending. She was standing taller, prouder, more confident. Lea smiled and said, "Now go make it happen."

You're probably sitting there saying to yourself, how could a few words help me to believe more in myself? How can reading statements to myself make a difference in my work or life? The truth is that these are proven methods used throughout the world. Life coaches, therapists, and success gurus swear by the power of positive affirmations. Athletes, singers, and theatrical performers swear by the power of visualizing success. The focus is on rewriting the narratives we tell ourselves in our heads from negative to positive. The idea behind positive affirmations is they should be all about what makes you feel strong and confident and powerful. By reading them or saying them to yourself out loud you make them real. Oprah Winfrey used them to change her life, Arnold Schwarzenegger used them to build big muscles. Muhammad Ali thrived was the king of positive self-talk. US Women's soccer star Carli Lloyd is a master at visualization.

By voicing these power statements out loud, we hear them, we take them in, we process them in our brain. We visualize and speak success to ourselves. Remember how we receive and store data from the world so we know how to deal with situations in the future? By speaking positive affirmations out loud, we are processing this positive, successful data, and storing it in our brains. It's one of the only ways to replace the negative self-talk that so many of us are so good at. Think about it with yourself. How many times do you tell yourself you can't do something… or don't deserve it… or aren't smart enough… or not strong enough? We do it all the time. It's self-sabotage. We are destroying any chance we have to succeed by telling ourselves we suck. We too often see only our blemishes, flaws, and failures in the mirror.

It's all because we ultimately fear failure. This is a crippling, paralyzing fear. We don't want to look bad in front of others. We don't want people to say that we couldn't hack it. To save us from failure, we sabotage ourselves before we even start. You can't fail at something you never actually try, right? But even if we get past this starting point because we believe we can do something, as we meet issues and setbacks and roadblocks, we start to lose that belief in ourselves. We replace confidence with questions and doubts. We're paralyzed by the fear of failing. So, we literally stop believing. Instead we question everything we're doing, which sends our confidence sliding back into the doldrums of no confidence.

If we are living in fear or paralyzing ourselves with negative self-talk and a lack of belief in ourselves then we can't take action in our lives. We can't fire up our **Action Element of Leadership**. We can't move forward. We are stuck. So, write out those positive affirmations about how good you are at stuff and start reading them out loud to yourself. It will sound weird at first because it's like a different language that we haven't heard before. But you don't need Rosetta Stone to learn this language, you just have to take action...

The next day Taylor woke up with a vengeance. She felt empowered by her conversation the night before with Lea. Taylor had always been a super motivated person, it's what had helped her to do well in her athletic career. She had always been a hard worker, fully dedicated to making everything she wanted to happen in her life come true. And up until recently it seemed, everything she put her mind to, she achieved. It had started as a kid. Her goal was to get a college athletic scholarship... she earned it. In college she wanted to be a starter on the track and field team... she made it. She continued to set personal bests throughout her career. She was a woman of action at that time of her life. Always working. Always pushing. Nothing ever got in her way and any roadblock that was put up in front of her she would figure out how to either get through it or around it.

But her business was different. It wasn't like she hadn't ever struggled in life, but this was the first time she didn't know how to beat the struggle. She was stuck. She tried just putting her head down and working longer and harder. She tried meeting with friends to talk to them about their struggles as emerging entrepreneurs. She watched YouTube videos and went to business seminars. Everything to be a better businesswoman, but when it came down to putting it in action, it just never quite clicked right. She would make progress, but then it would come crashing down.

When she started the business, Taylor knew it wasn't going to be as easy as a stroll along the beach. She knew there would be issues and struggles. She had started the business a couple of years before because she had grown tired of working for someone else. She had been a part of a huge health and fitness company, but everything she did put money in their pockets, not her own. Plus they weren't using her skills and talent to the fullest. She was just a cog in a giant wheel. But she knew she could be more and do more.

She had felt great and empowered and confident in the months following her big move from working for someone to working for herself. She had a logo built and shirts made. She launched her website and began blogging. She made videos and developed workout programs that she could sell. She was free to do what she wanted, not what someone was telling her to do. She was so busy all the time with building and developing that she didn't care how many hours she was putting in. This was because she absolutely loved what she was doing. Everything was working out, but then the first big crash hit her like a Mack truck in the dark of night.

She had reeled in a big client, a company that was looking for a health and wellness consultant who could work with their staff on decreasing stress, finding work/life balance, and working in a healthier fashion. She was shocked to get such a big contract so new into her business launch. It was a huge step for her fledgling one-woman company. As excited as she was to build a custom program for their needs, it was the first time in her new business that she felt just a little worried about whether she could actually handle such a big new project and client. But she did what she knew how to do. She put her head down and just worked non-stop. She was the woman of action back then. Nothing could slow her down. Nothing could stop her from developing. She worked with the company to build a great program and launched it in a big workshop day that included all employees in the company. She felt so strong and confident as she stood on the stage. She worked the room and had great activities for the participants. At the end of the day she left feeling great.

A few weeks later as she was preparing for her next round of workshop days (they had been split up into three days so she could work with smaller groups and individual departments), she got an email from the HR department in the company. It was a day before she was to start three straight days of workshops for the company and they wanted to talk urgently. The call was not what she was expecting. The head of the company's HR department notified her that they were terminating her contract immediately. She was frozen in shock. When she tried to ask about the reasons for being fired, the director told her the contract stated that they could terminate her without cause. No answers. No reasons. Taylor was left with the feeling of failure and she didn't even know why she had failed. It felt like rock bottom.

When Taylor reached out to some of the employees who had attended the workshop, they shared with her that the company put all of the blame on Taylor and her program (a program which the company had approved and loved when she presented it to them weeks before the launch). After the first workshop, management told employees that Taylor didn't know what she was doing and that her company was too small to handle their needs. But one of the employees

Taylor talked to told her the truth. It had nothing to do with Taylor at all (even though she was being blamed), the truth was a small group of employees complained because they didn't want to change. They didn't want to have to do health and wellness workshops. So, the employees attacked her and instead of the company backing Taylor because it was what the company wanted for their employees, management told everyone that Taylor had gone rogue. It was a way for the company to save face with their employees. Blame it on the one-woman business who they could say was unqualified.

The loss of the contract had absolutely destroyed Taylor. It crushed her confidence. It smashed her belief that she could make it as a small business owner. She began to find doubt everywhere around her... behind every door... in every corner... constantly shadowing her. She felt horrible. She didn't even want to get out of bed. When people asked her about the program and the contract, because she had told everyone about her success in landing the big deal, she could barely muster a response. It didn't matter what she said to them, because when she looked in the mirror all she saw was a failure. The strong confident woman making her own way in the world was suddenly cowering in the corner of the room hoping no one would even notice her.

Confidence and belief in oneself can be fleeting. Situations, experiences, and people can cause our confidence to crash down. The slide spectrum comes into play because what causes us to lose our confidence is based on how much confidence we actually have. Basically, the less confidence you have, the less traumatic an event needs to be to make you lose your confidence (the low end of the confidence spectrum). On the other hand, the more confidence you have, the more traumatic the event will need to be in order for you to lose your confidence.

Take for example a middle student who has to go up in front of the class to recite a poem he had to memorize. Since he has not had any experience with doing this type of public speaking, he has very little confidence in his ability to succeed at the task. The first time some kid in the class rolls his eyes, or snickers, or makes a little negative comment, the kid who is reciting the poem will completely lose any miniscule confidence he might have mustered. Now on the other end of the spectrum, you would find a noted public speaker who gives big motivational talks (think Tony Robbins or someone of that ilk). They have done so many events with huge crowds that a single individual clowning them isn't traumatic enough to dull their confidence.

What we mean by all of this is that we often hear about people who are super confident who think they can't possibly lose their confidence. It's their calling card, and nothing can shake them. But no matter who you are and how confident you might be, there is a situation that could knock your confidence into smithereens. When such a massive blow is given to our confidence (like what happened to Taylor), it can be really difficult to come back. It's like we take an uppercut from Mike Tyson in the heavyweight title match and we just go down to the canvas. We don't want to get up. We don't want to face another punch. We cower on the canvas and wait for the bell to ring.

No one around us would be upset at us for quitting. We would just be another statistic. Think about the stats. Around 33% of startups close down in the first 2 years after opening. The numbers grow as the years go by with 50% of all start-ups closing within the first 5 years of their launch and around 70% closing within their first 10 years. Certain industries, like restaurants, have even higher rates of failure. Yikes! That could cause some fear, right? But the key here is that every one of these businesses began in confidence. Someone or some team of people believed so strongly in what they were doing that they went for it. But something got in the way. Some situation crushed their confidence.

And it isn't just in businesses where we see issues with confidence. It can happen in any walk of life. Think about the student who aced every class in high school only to show up to college and get barely passing grades in their first semester. What do you think happened to that confidence? Or the new parents with a brand-new baby at home who strongly believe in their abilities as parents. Then the baby gets a tiny little cold for the first time and the freak out show begins. Calls are made to grandma for help while confidence goes running out the door of their home.

Situation is the key word to remember here in the Action Element of Leadership. The reason is that situations and contexts that we face and the way in which we go at them are so important to our success as a leader. The way in which we deal with situations decides our fate as leaders. And the big secret that exists here is… each situation or context might require a different action from you as the leader. We simply cannot handle every situation the exact same way. We have to get that toolbelt out that Lea was talking about and figure out which of our skills or abilities we need in order to get through the situation. Because as leaders, we can't just lay in the ring after getting hit with the knockout punch, we have to find a way to get up before we're counted out.

The months following the loss of the big contract became a mishmash of lost opportunities, wasted time, and negative self-talk. The strong confident woman that was Taylor, got lost like a tiny boat in the middle of a hurricane. She was being tossed around by every situation that came up. She grew afraid to try for new contracts in fear of losing another one. She stopped building new programs because the voice inside her kept telling her they would fail too. She had lost her way. But after talking with Lea, she was ready to try a new method. Instead of just trying to do the same thing day in and day out hoping for a new result, it was time to change the narrative in her head. It was time to find her strength… her power… her passion for her business again.

Taylor remembered how Lea had said she needed to find her positivity again. She thought back to when she felt the most positive. It was when she was starting her new business. She felt great at that time because she was finally excited and passionate about life, the same way she had been when she was a competitive athlete. She had lost that competitiveness somewhere along the path of the post-college career world. Sitting in a cubicle at the health and fitness company was like being on the slowest treadmill in the world. Just step after step after step. No turns, no curves, no hills. Flat and boring as hell. If she didn't try something new, then the treadmill would never end. She had to take action to change her life. At the start she was all about action but what had changed…

What was it that I loved so much? It was how I could turn my passion for athletics into a way to make money. It was how I could help other women be

> stronger and more powerful. I work to empower others and yet I'm afraid to let go. I need to plug myself back into the power and fire up my passion again. Breathe in the power. Breathe out the fire.

Suddenly Taylor had an idea. She folded up her laptop and jumped up from her desk with the laptop and a pad of paper in tow. She quickly left her home office and walked over to the room where she kept her exercise equipment. She set her business stuff on the floor and picked up her yoga mat. She laid it out directly in front of her laptop and sat down on her mat in a basic Easy Pose. She smiled proudly…

> I'm strongest on my mat. I'm most confident on my mat. I can do anything from my mat. This is my power. If only Lea could see me now. I'm finding a way to bridge the two sides of my brain.

She pulled her laptop and paper closer to where she could reach them. It might have seemed weird to others that she would prefer her mat to a nice desk in her renovated home office. But she had realized her mat was where she felt strength. She felt like she could do anything she set her mind to on that mat. And it was time to believe again in her own abilities. She breathed in. Her confidence was building…

> I am strong. I am powerful. I am confident. I believe in myself. I am success. I am power. I am skill. I am ability. I am talent. I am who I am. No one can take that away from me. I am damn proud of who I am.

Taylor breathed out as though fire was spewing out of her. Her passion was rekindled. She was ready to do this. She began to write herself a note on the piece of paper. It was a letter to her future self. It was explaining who she was and what she was all about. Every time she started to feel the negative self-talk rising, she would focus on her breath and her posture. Her eyes would close, and she would lean her head back, pushing her chest out, and then she would breathe in deeply. In came the power, out went the fire. Then she would go back to writing. Soon she had filled several pages with her power letter to herself.

She had grown accustomed to hearing her inner voice telling her she couldn't hack it. It was the debilitating, negative devil on her shoulder. She had grown used to the depressive state it caused her. She had shut off the positive, empowering angel on her other side. She thought the little angel side had been completely buried under the weight of being fired. But it had been there the whole time. She just hadn't believed in that side in forever. But the letter forced her to name the positives. As she read the letter, the positivity popped out. Because it had always been there. It was just waiting for the spark. Like a sprinter on the track just waiting for that starting pistol to go off, her passion was ready to blast off...

Like Taylor, we often find ourselves in utter darkness in our lives. Nothing seems to be going right. Nothing seems to work. Nothing seems to go our way. We are buried in our own negativity. Failure sits with us and hovers over us. It traps us. It scares us. It paralyzes us. It's the monster plucked straight off a horror movie set. Waiting in the dark. Hanging in the shadows. So many times, we are trying to find the big giant light switch so we can flip it and eradicate the darkness (our negativity) in a single swoop. But this isn't realistic, because it can't just disappear in one flip of a switch (and the longer we wait the harder it is to get out of the darkness).

Instead of looking for the big giant light switch, start with lighting a single candle in the darkness. One single positive thought. Let that give your darkness a flicker of light. Soon you will see another candle and go ahead and light that one. Take it one candle at a time. Take it one positive emotion or feeling or thought at a time. You build light and momentum with each candle that is lit. Soon enough, the darkness will be balanced by the light of a thousand positives.

Rather than waiting for the monstrous failure to paralyze us in the darkness of negativity, we need to unleash the beast within us that fulfills our passion for life. The beast is action and it's breathing fire. This is what the Action Element of Leadership is all about. It's about lighting the fire in our chest that makes us feel and do and act. It makes us want to start running towards a better future. And the key is that the Action Element of Leadership is all about the ability to recognize the situations we face and know exactly what skill or talent or ability to use to get after it.

For Taylor, it's all about connecting the strength she felt on the mat with the struggles she had at her desk. Taylor never had issues in her business with the actual health and fitness concepts. She was great at that and she knew she was great at that. But when it came to running the books, paying taxes, shipping products, dealing with clients, and all the other heavy business stuff that a startup deals with, she struggled. She had never been to business school so how the hell was she supposed to know what to do? You might think her use of the mat sounds really hokie, but imagine it to be like that stuffed animal or blanket that you absolutely had to sleep with as a child. You had to have it because it made you feel comfortable, safe, and happy. Taylor's mat is exactly that. It calms her fears and makes her feel strong.

On top of connecting two varying sides of her being, Taylor is (without realizing it) trying to balance her Action Element of Leadership. She is working on self-discipline and self-confidence by working through the activities she has put in front of herself. She is taking control of the voice inside her that says she can't do it. She is rewriting her story. She is building confidence and composure through her letter to herself. We need to remind ourselves of who we are and what we are great at and what we love to do. We need to speak them into existence. We need to visualize the success. We need to unleash the fire-breathing beast within us.

Over the next few months, Taylor found herself working from her mat almost every day. Any chance she had to sit or lay on her mat as she worked on the business side of her company she did. She was continuing to keep with her regular yoga practice with Lea. And the best part was that she was really starting to believe in herself again. She was feeling confident again. She was feeling strong again. She was feeling powerful again. Anytime she started to question herself, she would set her laptop away and move into a yoga pose. She would connect with her breath and once she felt like she was breathing fire again, she would return to her work. Sure, it didn't make for the most effective use of time to have to take so many breaks, but it was exactly what she needed to do to keep moving towards success.

It wasn't perfect by any means because there were still days where she could feel her chakra out of balance. But she was learning how to adapt to those situations and find ways to either bust through them or to detour around them. But then the day came where her new feelings were really tested. For a couple of months, Taylor had been working on a new video training series for other entrepreneurial women like herself. It was the first new program she had developed since she had lost the big contract. She was trying to teach others what she had been learning about herself. She developed a workbook, planned activities, shot the instructional videos, and finalized the coolest graphics. She was only days away from officially launching the program. All she was waiting for was the final products to arrive from the manufacturer.

She heard the delivery truck come rumbling down the street and stop in front of her condo building. She popped out the door and bounded down the stairs filled with excitement. The driver began unloading several boxes of materials. After he had wheeled them up to her place and gotten her to sign off on the delivery, Taylor excitedly ripped the boxes open. She couldn't believe she had actually done it. Whereas for so long, she had been blocked from creating anything new, she had put it all together and found her strength and power again. She couldn't wait to see how they had turned out. She had a back order of customers who had already pre-ordered the program and were waiting for the official launch.

As she pulled out the top video from the first box, she couldn't believe what she saw. She quickly started to rifle through the box only to find that all the videos looked the exact same. It was simply unbelievable… and not in a good way. The cover design was printed sideways on every video box. Totally screwed up. Total amateur hour…

> Shit. This can't be happening. Not again. Why do I screw everything up? I can't get anything right. I can't believe this is happening to me. Why did I think this was going to be any different this time?

Taylor dropped the videos back in the box and took a step away. She retreated to a corner of the room where she then squatted down and put her head between her legs. Total and utter despair. She felt depressed. She just wanted to curl up and hide from the world again. She felt like crap. She was all hunched over and out of alignment. She recognized the old Taylor in that corner breaking down. But the new Taylor could control this, and she knew it. She stood up out of her squat and moved her shoulders up and back. She lifted her head and extended her spine into Mountain Pose. She moved her hands out in front of her and then brought them together into prayer hands…

> Breathe in power. Breathe out fire. I am strong. I am powerful. I am confident. I believe in myself. I'm not afraid of failure. I'm not scared of you anymore fear. You are nothing. I am strong. I am powerful. I am confident. I believe in myself.

She could feel her chest filling with the fire. She could handle this. Her toolbelt of skills could help her solve this. She knew a true leader wouldn't retreat and hide. A leader would step out in front, adapt, and make a win out of a perceived loss. She reached out and grabbed a video and looked at it again. Who really cares that the cover art is sideways, the video is still functional and maybe people would think it was some kind of new artsy trend with videos. She knew she could make it work because what was in the video was most important. She unwrapped the case and took out the DVD. She popped it into her player and fired up her laptop. As the video began to play, she found that it wasn't just the cover that was screwed up. Somehow the entire video was playing upside down on the screen as well…

> I can't believe this. I look like a vampire working out. I'm standing on the freakin' ceiling. But damn I look athletic and tough to be able to do that routine upside-down defying gravity completely. Well this is definitely unique. I might have to add a warning to not attempt this at home on your own though!

Taylor found herself breaking out in deep and utter laughter. She couldn't stop laughing at her vampire exercise routine. She shook her head as she continued to giggle. Maybe it was the old saying that you have to laugh to keep from crying, but inside of her she was filled with joy. She couldn't believe how she was feeling. Months before this type of mistake would have absolutely crushed her, but in this moment, she could only laugh at the sight. It didn't crush her or make her feel like the avalanche was hurtling down the mountain. She knew she could fix the problem because she had skills.

She looked down at her left arm and found just what she was looking for. Scrawled across the top inner edge of her left arm was the tattoo she had gotten inked a few weeks before. It stated exactly what she needed to hear at that moment...

I am strong. I am powerful.
I am confident. I believe in myself.

As leaders, so much of our ability to be successful is in relation to how we respond to issues that arise in our lives. This is what the Action Element of Leadership is all about. You see, this Element of Leadership focuses on the ways in which a leader responds actively to the situations and contexts that he or she faces. The premise is that there is no single way to lead. There is no perfect way to be a leader. There is no singular form of leadership that works for everything and everyone. Situations and contexts matter in leadership. They determine the type of leadership approach that would fit best at that moment in time.

We mentioned earlier about having a toolbelt of skills, strengths, and approaches that we can use as leaders. The toolbelt is necessary because it allows a leader to choose the right tool for each situation that he or she will face. At times we may need to make a great speech. Other times we may need to be positive with a follower so that they feel empowered. At times we have to get things done so we take a task-oriented approach. The key is that we not only have to have a full tool belt of options, but we also need to know when to best use each tool. When a leader is in balance with their Action Element of Leadership, they are doing just that. They have their toolbelt on, they know how to use their tools, and they know where each tool works best.

Action Element Leaders don't fear what may lay ahead because they are prepared and ready. This allows them to act accordingly. It's similar to the way in which we connect certain music with particular aspects of life. Sometimes you need the soft, jazzy stylings of Kenny G to ease your mind and open your abilities to think deeply. Other times you need some pump-up music, whether it's Hip Hop or Heavy Metal, so that you can feel the energy coursing through you. Or it's a smooth R & B song to get you in the mood for romance. Mix the music up with a different situation or try to play multiple songs at the same time (multi-tasking) and you have a complete mess on your hands, and nothing sounds good. It's the same for the Action Element of Leadership. It's all about finding harmony and balance and not doing everything at the same time. Because that never ever works.

In the case of Taylor, at the beginning of this story she was taking the same approach to everything that was put in front of her in terms of her business. Because of the traumatic event she faced, she had stopped trying anything new or different. But here at this point, she is faced with a similar traumatic event. It was going to be her big new move for her business, and she had worked so hard to get there. But instead of retreating into the rut of previous experiences when the videos were screwed up, she tried a new tool from her belt. Instead of freaking out and falling apart, she took the whole thing in stride. Calm. Strong. Harmonious.

Harmony is a central tenant of this Element of Leadership, just as it is with the third chakra, known as the fire or solar plexus chakra. This chakra concentrates on self-discipline, making conscious choices, will power, and decision-making. When a leader is in balance with the Action Element, they are in control of their actions, abilities, and skills. They balance when and where to use each of them. They balance their emotions and they breathe in power and breathe out fire. Because with the spark of fire they launch their action forward ready to take on any situation the world throws at them. They have the ability to make decisions and then take action. That is the calling card of the Action Element Leader.

Taylor didn't waste time pulling out her phone and calling the manufacturing company. She sent them pictures of the video covers and her laptop screen where the video was playing. She stayed calm and took the approach of strength when dealing with the manufacturer. She didn't fly off the handle or go crazy with anger. She knew that wasn't going to solve anything. She talked her way through it, thinking about how her approach could help or hurt the situation. After several calls, the company told her they would be redoing the materials and rushing her order out asap.

Taylor felt great about how she had dealt with the situation. Outside of a few short moments spent on the edge of losing her cool when she first opened the box, she instead handled the entire situation as she now knew she could. As she stood up from where she had been making her calls, she looked down at the ground. Her mat wasn't there. She looked around and saw it rolled up in the corner. She laughed to herself at the thought that she just handled her business like a true leader, and she didn't even need her mat. She felt like that kid who finally tells her mommy that she doesn't need her teddy bear anymore because she's all grown up now.

Taylor's original plan to spend the afternoon prepping her orders to send out to her customers was now completely shot. Knowing she now had the day free she grabbed her mat and left her condo to walk over to Lea's Life Studio. As she strolled into the studio, she found Lea setting up for the next session. Taylor was a little early, so she started helping Lea to set out mats and prep the boards in the room. Taylor said, "Hey Lea, you won't believe what happened to me today!" Lea stopped and looked at Taylor who had begun laughing as she recounted the vampire exercise videos.

"Sounds like a time where the old T would have totally lost it," said Lea. Taylor shook her head with a big smile on her face, "Not this time. This girl stood in there like a champ. I reached to that toolbelt and found just the right skill to deal with it like a strong leader would." Lea nodded her head and said, "Sounds like someone is ready for the perfect yoga pose for a strong, confident leader. You want to try it?" Taylor nodded knowing she was always ready for a challenge.

Lea continued on, "Spread your feet out wide and turn your toes out slightly. Now bend your knees and squat down so that your upper leg is parallel with the ground below you. Now extend those arms straight out to your sides, but parallel with the ground. Face those palms towards me. Yeah that's it right there. Now bend those arms at your elbows and lift those hands up above you keeping your elbows at that angle. Look straight ahead and breathe in the power and confidence. Right like that. Now breath out that fire. The Goddess Pose just fits you perfectly T, don't you agree?"

Taylor smiled as she could feel the power coursing through her body. She stood up and gave a huge hug to Lea. "Thanks for helping me find myself again. I want to be just like you when I grow up." Lea burst out in laughter at the words. Taylor then asked Lea, "By the way, would you mind if I wrote the mantra on the board for today? I know exactly what to say." Lea handed over the pen and Taylor wrote…

I am strong. I am powerful.
I am confident. I believe in myself.

The Compassion Element

"Of course, I can get you those numbers Mr. Cardoso. I'll be right back," said Esteban as he walked out of the office to find the files. It was a regular part of the day. As CEO of one of the largest construction companies in the country, Mr. Cardoso was all about numbers. Everything he could read, hear, and see. He was into numbers because that was the way it had always been for him. Mr. Cardoso considered himself old school. He was a self-made man. No handouts from some rich uncle or father. He believed in outworking everyone around him. It was a mentality he had learned from his parents who had worked every day of their lives.

Mr. Cardoso had grown up with nothing... literally almost nothing. He and his parents were immigrants. His mother and father had worked a long series of rotating jobs, often times several at the same time. No career path, just moving from position to position trying to make ends meet. As a child, Mr. Cardoso had been teased and bullied by other kids in school, on the sports fields, and in his neighborhood. They made him feel different. They made him feel less than.

As a young kid, Mr. Cardoso promised himself that he would do everything he could to have money. As a teenager, he dreamed of a day when he would have his own family and they would never lack for money or nice things. He told himself he would win in life. His parents wouldn't be able to pay for college. His parents wouldn't be able to loan him money to start a business. He was going to have to do it on his own. But he was going to show all those other kids that he was better than what they thought of him.

And that is exactly what Mr. Cardoso did throughout his life. He worked and worked and worked. He excelled in the classroom and earned himself a scholarship to college. While in college, he didn't socialize or hang out as much as his friends did. He would have time for that once he had made it in life. He studied and worked constantly. It was the way his parents had shown him. He wasn't going to waste the opportunity he had in front of him.

With the first paycheck he earned for working his student job at the library, he went out and bought the first suit he ever owned. It wasn't the nicest or the flashiest, but it sure was better than anything else he had ever owned. That first suit helped him land his first internship with a small construction company near his college. He was the first one on site every morning and the last one to leave at night. He used every moment in the internship to shake hands and introduce himself to everyone he could meet. He knew that every person could potentially help him keep the promise he had made to himself when he was just a kid.

That internship turned into job after job in college. He was getting his name known because of how hard he worked. Every morning when he woke up, he told himself he would win that day. No matter who stood in his way, he would outwork them, outsmart them, and win. With every new position he got, he would use his first paycheck to buy a new and fancier suit. He told himself that to run with the big boys he was going to have to dress like the big boys.

The years after college followed the same trajectory. He used each new job to catapult himself up the corporate ladder. The pattern was so similar through his rise that he often thought of his path as though he was a hamster on a wheel. Just spinning around and around as he continued to run towards the promise he had made to himself as a kid. He was making money at every step. Every decision he made seemed to bring in more money and resources for the bosses. Every development he managed went straight to the top. He rode the bottom line like a rocket ship to the top of not only one organization, but seemingly the entire industry.

Through it all, he held to one mantra the he was going to make his childhood promise come true. There was no time to do anything else. He was all about winning.

"Here are the numbers, Mr. Cardoso," Esteban said as he came rushing back into the office. "Great looking suit, sir." Mr. Cardoso gruffly thanked the kid, but barely looked up as Esteban dropped the folder onto his desk in front of him. Esteban left the room and Mr. Cardoso began pouring through the latest reports. Everything was looking good as always. He got up from his desk to walk down to the company's vice president to ask about a blueprint for a new condo project. As he was walking out of the room, he caught a glance of himself in the mirror by his door…

> The kid is right, this suit does look good. It's probably worth more than what I am paying that kid. What a far cry from that first department store piece of crap suit I bought in college. And to think I thought that suit was everything. If only that version of me could see me now. He would be super impressed.

Mr. Cardoso knew titans of industry personally. He dined with presidents. He golfed with Fortune 500 CEOs. He was featured on Ted Talks, talk shows, newspapers, magazines… he was everywhere. He was the role model for how to make money and lots and lots and lots of it. There were thousands of people, if not millions, who wanted to be like Mr.

Cardoso. His company had built some of the best and biggest projects in the nation. From skyscrapers to resorts, condos to shopping centers, his company was at the top. Everybody wanted his success, his cars, his house, his life.

As Mr. Cardoso walked through the company headquarters, he looked around at all the cubicles and offices scattered throughout. He didn't see a single face looking at him as every head was buried down staring at their computer screens. As he went by the coffee station in the break room, no one was milling around chatting. The room was empty, save for the pot of coffee that smelled rather stale. Everything was just as he wanted to see it and hear it. No wasted time. No chit chatting. No music. No socializing. No laughter. No time off task. No parties or celebrations. No wasted energy. It was all about efficiency. It was all about structure. There were expectations to work when you were at work. His long-standing mantra was that "You hang out on your own time, not on Cardoso's dime." And it wasn't just a phrase, it was real for no one wanted to get caught socializing by the big boss himself. They feared Cardoso.

If an outsider was to walk into the building where the company was located, they would have turned around and walked back out thinking they had mistakenly walked into a public library. Dead quiet. Staff meetings were as matter of fact as they could be. It was just business. One item on the agenda after another. Move, move, move. No time to talk things out. When your name was called, you reported out on your project or department. No need for fine details either. It was as though Dragnet's Sgt. Joe Friday was saying in his monotone voice, "Just the facts, ma'am. Just the facts."

The environment was what it was. Stale. Boring. Dull. Blah. This wasn't Google or Yahoo or any other newfangled techy hippie company as Mr. Cardoso liked to call them. This was a construction company. There was nothing new age about this place. Nothing innovative. It was as though they had plucked the company headquarters out of Henry Ford's production line in the 1930s. It was a bunch of cogs in a machine and if you didn't like it, they would find a new cog to fill your place. Tons of new employees had come and gone over the years, a constant turnover like a New York subway turnstile. Outside of a few stalwarts who had been with Cardoso since the beginning, seemingly everyone else who had ever worked for him rarely lasted even a year.

Some might think that Mr. Cardoso was a complete jerk, and nobody liked him. But this wasn't the case. He really wasn't overly jerky, but he wasn't overly nice either. He was the boss. He was direct. He was straightforward. He expected a lot out of his employees because he expected a lot of himself as well. And all of this was fine. It's what had helped him find success. He knew how to win. Man, oh man, did he know how to win. Money. Finances. Condos. Hotels. Office buildings. Wins. Wins. Wins. Who could argue with success? Mr. Cardoso was holding to that promise he had made so many years before… he was going to make it in life.

Does this story sound familiar to you? Well maybe not the fancy suits and more money than you know what to do with. But how often do we get solely focused on a goal that we'll do anything to make it happen? How often are we told by society that we're going to be nothing? How often does the story seem written against us? How often do we tell ourselves we're going to prove everyone wrong? When we get into this mode, we hope that nothing can ever stop us, but too often other aspects of life get in our way.

This didn't happen for Mr. Cardoso. He was single, having rarely even dated. He had no hobbies or ways to escape from business and work. It's what he told himself he had to do to make it in life. It was the narrative he wrote for his life. But doesn't it feel like something is missing from his life? Doesn't it feel that despite all the money and success and status that he earned, there is a void in other areas of his life? Is there more to life that he is missing because he is so focused on the path he set forth? He is clearly a leader, as he has successfully led company after company to win after win.

His career is a testament to his leadership. He clearly has leadership skills and uses them for success. While it's easy to see that Mr. Cardoso is a leader, the question that arises is whether he is a complete leader?

What we mean by that is that there is clearly something missing in his leadership. Can you see what is missing? It's the ethics. It's the morals. It's the values. This isn't to say that he is a cheat or has cut corners to get to the top. Mr. Cardoso has never done anything dishonest or unethical in his business practice. When we talk ethics as a society, we often focus on what is moral or right, but he hasn't done anything wrong in that sense. What is missing and what we mean by an ethical leader is one that has compassion for others, especially followers. Some of you may laugh at this…

> What the hell are you talking about? If the company is making money, then everybody is making money. If the company is winning, then everybody is winning. Isn't he taking care of others by taking care of his company? What gives?

If this were the case, why would so many people be leaving the company? It's because of the environment. It's about wellness and love and care. It's about serving the needs of others, not just your own. To care for others doesn't mean you have to trade in success or wins. You don't have to be a non-profit organization saving some endangered duck-bill platypus to care for others. But shouldn't there be more to success than simply counting the piles of money?

A perfect example of the difference in leadership comes from The Karate Kid (no not the newer version, but the old school fantastic Ralph Macchio version). We think of Mr. Miyagi as the ultimate leader (and he was), but the part we miss is something most of us don't want to hear. Ready for it... the mean sensei John Kreese of the Cobra Kai dojo was also an *effective leader*. Shocking, right? But it's true. Both of these men taught kids karate skills and prepared them to win. Their students followed their every word and every action. Wherever these men wanted the boys to go, and whatever they wanted them to do, the boys would follow.

But what then is the difference in their leadership? It's the ethics, the morals, and the values. It's their compassion for others. In the Cobra Kai dojo, it was all about winning at any price... cheating, fighting dirty, it was all good, as long as you win right? It's leadership, but it's scary leadership. But the wise old Mr. Miyagi is the *master* leader because he was developing more in Daniel LaRusso than just the ability to beat an opponent. For Miyagi, his training was about being a better person, a better human being, not just winning a fight. That is leading in the **Compassion Element of Leadership**. Mr. Miyagi's leadership makes a difference...

and not just in being able to catch flies with a pair of chopsticks… although that is pretty cool too.

You know the old saying, "Stop and smell the roses." It fits perfectly here. While Mr. Cardoso is running the path towards success – and the promise he made himself as a young boy – has he ever slowed enough to smell the roses? Too often we think our leadership is solely focused on winning, on building the bottom line. We care about finances. We care about money. We want to win. It doesn't matter who we have to run over to get there. But what if we ever stopped to smell the roses? Would it mean we couldn't win? Does it mean we wouldn't be successful? Or could it be a chance to experience something beautiful and amazing in our lives? Could it make us happier in life? Could it become a different form of leadership that we need? Is there more to life than just winning and making money?

Later that afternoon, Esteban reminded Mr. Cardoso of his doctor's appointment. Mr. Cardoso was pissed that he had to leave the office. He didn't want to go, but he couldn't get a refill on his blood pressure meds without seeing his doctor once a year. The appointment went the same as so many before that. Dr. Mallett talked about the same things he always talked about. He wanted Mr. Cardoso to relax more, take some time off work, maybe even spend time doing some hobbies. He wanted him to spend more time with friends and family. All of this in an effort to destress. All of this to unwind a little bit. Dr. Mallett even said to him, "Work shouldn't be everything in your life. It's not healthy for you." Mr. Cardoso smirked slyly and said, "Sure Doc, you got it." But Cardoso knew he wasn't going to do any of it. What the hell did this doctor know about running a business? Why doesn't he just stick to the health stuff... the last thing Mr. Cardoso needed was some new age life coach.

"Can't you just prescribe some med that can help me destress?" asked Mr. Cardoso in a joking manner. "You've got it," Dr. Mallett said as he pulled out his little prescription pad and started scribbling out a quick few words. Mr. Cardoso couldn't believe it had worked. Dr. Mallett handed over the prescription note as he said, "You have to promise to give this a try, I think it's just what you need in your life."

Yoga 3x per week
See Yogi Lea at Lea's Life Studio

Dr. Lou Mallet

Mr. Cardoso wanted to crumple it up and throw the stupid prescription away. He had never seen such a dumb idea. But he knew how to be political… he had done it his whole career. He held the note in his hand and promised Dr. Mallet he would take him up on the order and try it out. As he left the office, Mr. Cardoso knew he had done what he had done hundreds of times before. Tell someone something they wanted to hear to get them to back off and leave him alone. As he walked down the medical center hallway, he crumpled up the paper and noticed a trashcan sitting in the little café at the end of the building…

> Perfect, I can toss this stupid thing away and grab a coffee for my way back to work. What a waste of time this entire afternoon has been.

As he drew in close to the trashcan with the balled-up yoga prescription in his hand, he heard his name being called, "Mr. Cardoso…. is that you?" He turned to see a man sitting in a wheelchair in the corner of the café.

> Crap. Who the hell is this? I just want to get some coffee and get back to work. I have got to get out of here. Just talk to him really quick and be on your way. You can grab coffee on the drive back.

"Wow I can't believe it. Theeeee Mr. Cardoso is in the same little café as me," said the man through a wry smile. As Mr. Cardoso moved closer to the man, the man said, "You probably don't recognize me anymore... it's been a long time. It's Alex Samson." Mr. Cardoso recognized the name immediately. He couldn't believe it. Samson and Cardoso had started as interns together decades ago in college. They had stayed in touch for a while as both were building their business careers. Mr. Cardoso had even attended Samson's wedding so many years ago. But since then, the men had lost touch. He could remember that Samson had tried to reach out several times, but Mr. Cardoso kept tucking the notes and messages away saying he would get back to him after the next project. But there was always another project...

"Hey Mr. Samson, it's good to see you. It's been forever since I last saw you," said Mr. Cardoso as he reached out to shake hands. Alex reached out and lightly grasped Cardoso's outstretched hand. He looked like he could barely move his arm. "No worries," said Samson, "You had a lot bigger things to worry about then an old college buddy. I was watching one of your TedTalks the other day remembering the good ol' days when we were just a couple of kids trying to figure out how to get the bosses their coffee!" Both men started to laugh. Samson's laugh ended abruptly in a coughing fit. "What are you doing here anyways Mr. Samson, and what's up with the wheels?"

"Oh, just here for a little procedure. The doctors won't let me drink coffee anymore because of my heart, but I just love the smell of it, so I sit down here to enjoy the aromas." It was then that Mr. Samson shared what he had been up to. He was in the hospital for yet another surgery. He was having heart trouble and had already been through several bypass and artery surgeries. His heart was simply giving out. His doctors blamed it on a bad mix of genetics, stress, and unhealthy habits. Samson shared how he had pushed so hard to keep up with Mr. Cardoso. That he wanted to be as successful, to be as well known, to be the best. He was always working. He was always trying to win. But the grind had taken a serious toll on his health and life and happiness.

The story that Mr. Samson shared only seemed to get worse with every sentence. He had his first heart attack about a decade before. It was while he was giving a huge presentation to his board. The last ten years had found him in and out of the hospital. When Mr. Cardoso had asked how the family was handling it, Samson shared that his wife had left him many years before his first heart attack. She had been fed up with him being disconnected and always working so many hours while never being home.

When Mr. Cardoso asked him about his kids, Samson shared that he barely ever saw them. He had never taken the time to be with them when they were young, because he was making money so they could have everything they ever needed. But it had left a void, one that he could not seem to cross now. Mr. Cardoso could see the tears streaming from Samson's eyes when he talked about his kids. Samson shared that he was living alone, rarely even seeing friends because he had pushed so many away over the years.

"Time to go upstairs, Mr. Samson," said a nurse who had entered the café without even being noticed. She took hold of the wheelchair and began to wheel him away, but he turned back. "It really was good to see you Mr. Cardoso. I hope that all is well with you. Would love to hear about you sometime. Maybe we can get together soon," said Samson as they wheeled him away. Mr. Cardoso smiled and said, "That would be great old friend."

In the old days in sports like boxing and football, if athletes got knocked out, the athletic trainer would wave smelling salts in front of their noses. The salts worked to shock the system back into working. It was a quick hit change that would wake the athlete up. It didn't mean they were totally all together in the head at that point, but it at least woke them up with a jolt. Sometimes our lives put smelling salts right in front of our nose. It causes us to jolt awake and suddenly see the world around us. Most of the time, life's smelling salts are fear-inducing moments that make us rethink how we are doing things, seeing things, or understanding things. It can take many forms from a car accident to a job loss, an illness to the death of a friend. No matter what it is, it wakes us up.

Mr. Cardoso got a dose of life's smelling salts when he ran into Mr. Samson. He didn't like what he saw. He didn't like what he heard. He hated to see what his friend was going through. It made him suddenly and instantly aware of his own life. This is what these moments do to us. They show a giant mirror back at us. But instead of showing the amazing, wonderful, positive aspects of our life, this mirror shows all the warts and issues that are plaguing us. Think of the Evil Queen in Snow White, but instead of asking the mirror who is the fairest in the land, instead we ask it, "Mirror, mirror on the wall, what the hell is wrong with me and my life?"

Mr. Cardoso didn't like what he saw in the mirror. Samson was Cardoso. Cardoso was Samson. There were differences, such as Samson got married while Cardoso never did, or that Cardoso's business was worth way more than Samson's. But when you scrape all of the periphery away, would it not be the same? Who would be in that hospital with Cardoso, if the roles were reversed? Would he have family there? Would he have friends there? Would he have coworkers and employees there? Would anybody care about it him at all?

While it's difficult to think about in terms of our own lives, who would be there for us if we were in that hospital? Would our family, friends, coworkers, or employees be there? While we may often blame others for not being a part of our lives, we have to look in that mirror and see what we have done wrong to push others away. Have we worked too hard to be successful? Have we not had time for others because we had to work? Have we skipped parties and gatherings and happy hours because we had to keep working?

We're not saying give up and stop working completely! We are also not saying just go party all the time... no not at all. But life is about balance. No money or financial success is worth cutting the ties to the people in our life who will be there in that hospital with us. No money or financial success is worth not having love and compassion in our lives. But the question we all struggle with is how can we find that balance? Doesn't something have to give to make it all work?

Seeing Mr. Samson scared the hell out of Mr. Cardoso. He suddenly didn't want to go back to work that day. He couldn't remember the last time he had taken an afternoon off, but he was all shook up. He couldn't go back. He texted Esteban and let him know he was taking the rest of the day off. He assured him that everything was okay (because Esteban was freaking out thinking something was really wrong if the boss was not working). Mr. Cardoso climbed into his Lamborghini and left the hospital parking lot. He didn't know where he was going, he just needed to go. He was so shaken up. He was freaking out. He didn't know what to do. He found himself just driving around the city. Nowhere really to go. Nothing really to do. He had no idea where he even was at that point. He kept thinking about Samson. He kept thinking about his own life…

"*BEEEEEEEEEEEEEPPPPPP*! A blaring car horn pulled him out of his daze. He looked in his mirror and saw a young twenty-something year old in a big lifted truck throwing his hands up and honking his horn. Mr. Cardoso looked up at the light and realized it had turned green while he was sitting there. He pulled through the intersection with the young guy right on his bumper. Not wanting to get hit by the road rager behind him, Mr. Cardoso pulled off at the first driveway he saw coming off the road. He had to get away from the guy. He pulled into the lot and parked in the first open spot he found. He turned off his car and took a deep breath…

> What the hell is going on with me? Samson isn't me. That would never happen to me. I know what I'm doing. That won't be me. Shit, what if that is me? What the hell am I supposed to do?

He was completely lost, not only on his drive, but in his life. He wanted to talk to someone about it, but as he scrolled through his phone contacts, he realized there wasn't a single person he could actually talk to. He just wasn't that close with any of them anymore…

If only Mom was still alive. I could call her. She would understand. She would listen to me. She would help me. She was always there for me. I miss her so much.

Completely distraught, he looked up out of his car to at least figure out where he was. Maybe he could find a bar and sit down with a cold beer and think. As he looked up, he saw that he was parked in front of a little old building that could use some real remodeling. The sign on the front, painted in old hand carved letters read…

LEA'S LIFE STUDIO

He shook his head as he laughed softly to himself. He felt tears rolling down his face. He reached down into his pocket and felt the crumpled ball of paper in it. He took it and found the prescription note that he had meant to throw away until he ran into his old friend. He laughed again as the tears continued to stream onto his cheeks. This was the place that Dr. Mallett had prescribed for him. It was one of those weird moments in life. Like something had led him here.

But he couldn't get up the courage to walk in. He sat in the car for a while. He didn't know what to do. He had always been so poised in business. He could walk into any room and sell anything to anyone, but now he was frozen. As Mr. Cardoso sat staring at the studio, he heard a soft voice speaking to him from outside the car, "Trust me, it's not as scary as it looks." He turned to see a small older lady standing just outside the car. "The first step is always the hardest in life, but I promise you will find whatever you are looking for right inside those doors. Make life count. All you have to do is to walk in the door." The woman smiled and walked away and into the studio.

> This is getting way too weird. Like Twilight Zone weird. Who was that woman and how did she know what I was thinking? What the hell is going on here? I guess I'm meant to go in those doors. I guess it wouldn't hurt to pick up a brochure or something and then come back later to workout.

When Mr. Cardoso walked in through the doors, a young woman smiled and extended a rolled-up mat to him as she said, "Lea said you would be coming in the door and might need a mat." Mr. Cardoso replied, "No, no I'm not here for a class. I just want to get some info, maybe a brochure." She smiled, "We don't have any brochures, because the best way to get info is to try it out. You took the first step, why not take a few more." Mr. Cardoso stammered out a reply, "But I don't have any workout gear. I'm in a suit…" The young woman smiled and said, "It's okay. There's no set uniform. We welcome all, even businessmen in fancy suits."

Mr. Cardoso now found himself walking into the room with a mat in his arms. He looked around the room and saw the old lady who had talked to him at his car. She smiled at him and waved. He smiled back sheepishly and moved to the back. He set his mat down and then took his shoes, belt, and coat, and piled them neatly next to his mat...

> This will teach me to take an afternoon off from work. What the hell am I doing here? I don't even know the first thing about yoga. I look like an idiot the way I'm dressed. There's no way I can do yoga.

The older lady, who he soon realized was Lea of Lea's Life Studio, began the class and he did his best to try to keep up. He was definitely out of sorts. This was not a feeling he liked. He had worked his entire life to try to prove himself as the best, but clearly, he was not the best at this. Everybody else in the room seemed so good at yoga, he knew he must have stood out like a sore thumb. And he hated that feeling. It's what he had been trying to escape since he was a little kid.

Later in the class, as he was struggling to find any sort of balance whatsoever, Lea came over to his mat. He stopped his movements and looked up at her. She had leaned in close, "What is your name friend?" "Mr. Cardoso," he replied out of habit. Lea giggled, "No, no, we don't use titles here, because titles are just roadblocks to keep people away. Here, we are all friends. So, what's your real name?"

> What a bunch of hippie bullshit that is. I knew this place would be like that. Nobody calls me by my first name. These people aren't my friends and even if they were, they'd still have to call me Mr. Cardoso. I deserve respect. I deserve to be called Mr. Cardoso.

But as Mr. Cardoso looked at Lea's sweet smiling face, the anger just left his thoughts. He took a deep breath and then he couldn't help himself but say, "Miguel…" She smiled and clapped happily, "I am so happy to see you here Miguel! Don't worry about the moves today. Focus on what is most important in your life. Remember to make your life count. Breathe out love, kindness, and compassion." He looked down in embarrassment because he wasn't sure if he had anything to actually think about in those areas. He couldn't remember the last time he'd seen any of his friends. He hadn't spoken to his siblings since his mother died. He wasn't sure if he had ever really felt love or compassion for anyone other than his family.

As with many things in our lives, when we let things go for a long time, we really struggle to get them started again. This happens with friends, exercise, hobbies, habits, and all sorts of other things. We often don't mean to let things go sliding away, but they just do. A day turns into a week. A week into a month. A month into a year. A year into a decade. And so on, and so on, until eternity. We lose track of time. We lose track of the importance of those things in our lives. We disconnect and move on. After a while we feel like even if we wanted to reconnect, we wouldn't know where to start.

Think about an old friend of yours, maybe from your childhood, or a college roommate. You two were the best of friends and did everything together, but as you think about that person, can you even remember the last time you talked to them? Sometimes it's because of some kind of fight or argument. Or it's that your lives went in different directions. Or it's just that you got busy living and didn't have time. But no matter the reason, you've lost contact, you've fallen apart. You've probably thought to yourself on many occasions that you should reach out and reconnect but you're too embarrassed or you have no idea where to even begin.

As Lea told Miguel, the first step is always the hardest. But the embarrassment and the fear that blocks us from taking that first step is just the narrative we're writing. It's our way of living in a little protected shell. It's our way of blocking ourselves off from the world. It's our way of blocking out the happiness that could be there. We make all sorts of excuses in our narrative to keep people away. The excuses might make sense, but who are they hurting? Who are they blocking? What are they taking away from our lives? That first step will be hard, but it's worth it in the long run.

Because as leaders we need to learn how to build those bridges. We need to have other people in our life. We need the enrichment that caring for others brings to our lives. We need the softness of these relationships to offer respite from the stark, harsh world we often face on a daily basis. We need not fear a single hard step that might open a beautiful and serene and happy path for our lives. So, take that step. Make that call. Send that text. Knock on that door. It's worth it.

At the end of the session, Miguel walked up to the young lady to give her back the mat. He felt a tap on his shoulder and turned around to find Lea at his side. "So how did it go with your reflection, Miguel?" He was thrown off by hearing his first name. It had been so long since he'd heard someone use it. He shook his head to let her know it had not gone well. Lea smiled at him and said, "That's okay Miguel. The fact that you took the step to even try says a lot about you. Just know that everything in your life can be changed. You can find it out there if you first find it in you. Make your life count. Breathe out love, kindness, and compassion. I can't wait to see you again soon."

Miguel left the building with his head cloudy from all the thoughts going through his mind. It was like the kids always say… *mind blown*. There was so much going on. There was so much to think about. As he got into his car and began to drive home, he couldn't stop thinking about his family. It had been months since he had last spoken to them. Their mom had always been the glue holding the family together, but with her gone, the connection was lost. As he thought about his siblings, he couldn't stop thinking about his dad...

What the hell is going on with me? Why am I so emotional? Why am I crying? I never get emotional. I'm not this weak. What did the yoga do to me?

Minutes later he found himself pulling up in front of his dad's house, a beautiful home Miguel's company had built for his parents. It was his way of thanking them for their sacrifices so he could get to where he was. He had moved them out of the old neighborhood and finally into a nice home in the suburbs. But Miguel hadn't been there in a long time. It just wasn't the same without his mom around.

As he pulled up, Miguel saw his dad standing out in front of the house watering flowers. His dad had his headphones on, which meant he was listening to the ballgame, something he loved to do. The tears that had been welling up on the drive to the house came pouring down Miguel's face as he got out of the car. His dad turned around and set the hose down. He and Miguel met each other in the middle of the grass with a huge hug. Miguel suddenly didn't care what anyone else thought of him in that moment. He didn't care who saw him.

Miguel stood hugging his dad and crying on his shoulder. "I'm sorry I haven't been around Pop…" Miguel stammered out, but his dad shushed him as he said, "Stop apologizing son, it doesn't matter. You're here now. That's all that matters." Dad and son spent the rest of the evening sitting on the porch sipping beers and talking about old times.

Later on, Miguel's father went into the house and returned with an old piece of lined yellow paper, ripped and crumpled in places. He handed it to Miguel, "I have saved this for a long time. Never forget who you really are." Miguel looked down and immediately recognized it as the note he had written when he was about nine or ten years old promising himself about his future. It had been the driving force in life.

> I'm Miguel Cardoso. I promise I'll grow up to make the world better. I promise I'll make so much money my parents never work again + get new house + my brother and sisters have all the toys they ever want. I promise I'll make so much money I get married + have kids + we go to resturaunts + on vacations to cool places. I promise I'll make enough money to help + fix up my neighburhood so it's better. I promise I'll give money to poor people like my friends. I promise I'll help kids who get picked on like me. I promise I'll help people so they don't have a life like I do.

The note wasn't as he remembered. He had forgotten all the stuff about making his family better and making the world and his neighborhood a better place. He had always just focused on the making money part. He had forgotten the *why* behind it. He went over to his dad and kissed him on his forehead, "Thanks Pop. I gotta go. I got promises to keep."

The next morning, Miguel called his assistant Esteban to tell him he would be taking a sick day. Miguel got dressed in some exercise attire and drove himself over to Lea's Life Studio. He got out and went to the door, only to find it locked. He stood outside with a big group of people who were also waiting for class. When Lea opened the doors and everyone filed in, she stopped Miguel and smiled, "Back again so soon? You'll find it much easier now that you aren't in a suit!" Miguel smiled for the first time in a long time.

During the session, Miguel really connected with certain moves including the Cobra Pose, Fish Pose, and Warrior One Pose. He could feel the connection to his heart in those poses. It felt good to feel good again. He was ready to change his world, but he knew he had to change himself first…

Make my life count.
Breathe out love, kindness, and compassion.

Sometimes we get so stuck in a rut of life that we can't break away from it. We fear losing out or falling behind if we were to take some time away for ourselves. But as Miguel finds in this story, we all need the time to reflect and reconnect to what Miguel refers to as his *soft* side. While Miguel may think of his emotional side as a weakness, it's not that at all. Our emotions and feelings can be a strength in our leadership practice. We all want to find love, kindness, and compassion. It's a fundamental need for our health and happiness and success. So, if the whole world needs this, why do so many leaders shy away from this side of who they are? It's because we get caught up in the bottom line... money. It's what we think about in determining if people *made it* in life.

Think about that high school reunion where everybody is asking about how you've done in life. They are sizing up your success. They ask what type of car you drive or where you've traveled in the world or what neighborhood you live in. They ask what title you have or what job you're in. All of this is a way for them to see if you were a success in life or not. It's to measure you up against themselves to see who *won* in life. Notice that no one ever asks what difference you made in the world. No one asks how happy you are or if you feel good about your life. No one asks how often you smile or laugh. No one asks how you truly are doing. See those things are not quantifiable. They don't help to put you in a box of either successful or not successful. But money and titles do.

The entire world seems to focus on the bottom line, but why does it have to be that way? There's nothing wrong with the bottom line. We don't want our businesses to close or for any of us to go bankrupt. We don't want to lose our homes. We don't want to starve. And yet where is the balance? What is the breaking point? We can focus on the bottom line if it is not separating us from what makes us happy and healthy in life. It can't separate us from fun and relaxation. It can't separate us from family, friends, love, care, or compassion.

This is the where the Compassion Element of Leadership comes in. It's the balance for our lives. It's the part of us that remembers that other people around us are important to. It's the part that reminds us that the environments we live in and work in are so important. Do we feel love and compassion? Do we feel the kindness and care we so desperately want in our lives? Is our work taking us away from our children, from our siblings, from our friends? Miguel was so focused on making money that could change the lives of everyone around him, that he forgot the whole part of using it to change their lives. Kind of a big important detail to miss! But as Lea told him, it's never too late to get started. It's never too late to take that first step. But can he really do it? Can you do it in your life? Can you lead with compassion?

That night, Miguel called in to Esteban and told him he would be out for the rest of the week. Miguel again reassured him nothing was wrong, but that he needed some time to take care of some personal matters. He would return to work after the weekend. During the rest of the week, Miguel found himself doing things he hadn't done in a long time. He called his brother and sisters. He visited his dad again and helped him mow his lawn, something he hadn't done since he was a teenager. Miguel went to one of Lea's yoga sessions every single day that week. The sessions were therapeutic for him, forcing him to sit and reflect on his life. The whole time he kept one mantra in mind – Make my life count. Breathe out love, kindness, and compassion.

He found himself back at the hospital visiting his old friend Alex Samson after his surgery. He even wheeled him down to the little café so they could smell the coffee together and talk about their old college days. They laughed and shared stories about their earliest days in business. They talked about life and love and what it all meant. At the end of the week, Miguel found himself driving down his old block where he had grown up. The neighborhood was even worse than he had remembered it. It was a showcase of poverty and of a part of the city that had long since been forgotten. He spent the afternoon walking the neighborhood, talking with people, and he even grabbed lunch at La Casita, a little hole-in-the-wall eatery which he had frequented as a teen.

On Monday morning, he was ready to get back to work. He wasn't going to let himself fall back into the old traps. He wasn't going to go back to the way things had been. When he got out of the shower and went to his walk-in closet, every wall was filled with fancy dress clothes, suits, loafers, the whole nine yards. But he walked right past them and went to the back corner where he kept his more casual looks. There he found a sharp looking green polo and a pair of nice jeans. He passed on the fancy Italian loafers and went with a pair of stylish sneakers. As he looked in the mirror, he couldn't even recognize himself. Miguel couldn't remember the last time he had gone to work without a suit on.

When he walked into the building that morning, the entire place seemed to stand still. It wasn't just how he was dressed, but the fact that he actually stopped and talked to the three executive assistants at the front desks and asked them about their families and their weekends. The assistants didn't know what to do, because normally he would just walk right by with a curt, "Good morning." But on this day, as he walked through the building, Miguel actually spoke to the people sitting in their cubicles. He greeted them and asked them how they were doing. People didn't know how to react.

When he got to his office, Esteban was there waiting. "It's good to see you Mr. Cardoso. Did everything go okay?" Miguel stopped and turned to face Esteban. He looked at the kid and said, "Thank you for asking about my week Esteban. It went *really* well. But there is one major issue we need to address." Esteban looked scared. His eyes opened wide because he knew whatever it was, it was not good. Mr. Cardoso was always grumpy on Mondays. But then Miguel smiled at Esteban, "Please stop calling me Mr. Cardoso. My name is Miguel." Esteban stuttered out a response, "But Mr. Cardoso… you said to never call you by your first name…" Miguel smiled at the young man, "Things are going to change around here and we're going to start with that. I am Miguel. I've always been Miguel. I lost my way for a little while. But I have found it again and I'm excited about it."

Esteban was dumbfounded by the turn of events. But as Esteban would soon find out, Miguel wasn't just talking the talk, he was walking the walk. Esteban watched as Miguel walked over to the wall to the side of his desk, the wall that contained all the great honors he had won. On the wall were pictures of him with presidents and famous celebrities, as well as plaques and awards the company had earned for prestigious designs and builds. But what was missing on that wall was any sort of emotion or feeling other than *pride*. And Miguel just didn't care about the pride anymore.

"Hey Esteban, can you come and help me take these down?" asked Miguel. Soon piles of plaques and awards and pictures were sitting in the corner of the office. Miguel opened a huge box that he had carried in that morning. He and Esteban started putting the framed pictures from inside the box up on the wall. There were pictures of Miguel's family, his parents, his childhood home. There were pictures of the various teams in the company that had worked on projects. Not the fancy ribbon cutting pictures, but the pictures of the employees working on the projects. These were the pictures that showed the heart of the company, not just the results. Miguel left the center of the wall completely open. Esteban asked him, "What's going in the middle, because we don't have any pictures left." Miguel turned and went to his briefcase. He pulled out one last frame. As he placed it up on the wall, he smiled at seeing his childhood promise note on the crumpled yellow paper staring right back at him.

The weeks and months that followed found Miguel making changes to the company in ways that no one thought possible. The changes took time, as he didn't want to push too much. But no expense was spared in making changes to their headquarters. Office cubicles came down and were replaced with large social tables and hidden coves so people could collaborate or just hang out. The break room was remodeled to make it more inviting and comfortable. Glass walls were installed in meeting rooms and offices.

As Miguel walked the floor months later, he could feel the difference. He could hear people laughing and talking… and not even about work. People were dressing more casually. Some of the assistants were setting up for a party to celebrate another project that had been completed. Staff meetings now always included a positivity segment where people would share a fun or inspiring story from their work in the field. Miguel had asked that people share about the difference they were making, and most importantly he wanted to know how their work was changing lives.

But the changes weren't just structural or procedural, the company began to open its doors to all clients. Whereas in the past, they only let the wealthiest and most influential clients into the building to bring projects to them, Miguel had actually started a team within the company that went out in communities talking to people and asking them about projects that were needed. The company even completed their first ever pro-bono project for a local area in the most need, something they would've never dreamed of before. The company was still making a nice profit on their work in total, but they were also making a difference in the world.

Early in this story, Miguel talked about his soft side… the emotional, compassionate, kind side of our beings is often referred to in this manner. It is often said in this way as a way to denounce it or to throw it away. Especially for the men out there, we often see this as a weakness. We don't want to let people see us cry or be emotional. It's not *manly* enough…. give us a break. Seriously, give us a break on this one. Whether we want to admit it or not, we all have a soft side. We all have emotions. We all need kindness and compassion in our lives. We all need love. We aren't talking about romantic love in this case (although that's a nice thing to have as well), but rather the love that we have for others. Family. Friends. Coworkers. Bosses. Strangers. This may sound mushy and gushy, but who doesn't think the world needs more compassion. More kindness. More love.

So, what does this have to do with leaders and leadership? Everything. All of it. Technically, according to leadership experts, a person can be a great and successful leader as long as they move a group of followers towards a shared common vision. Technically, leadership has nothing to do with the ethics of leadership meaning that you can be a successful leader when you lead a group who robs a bank. You had a shared vision and you successfully pulled it off. This is *effective* leadership. But what about the ethics, the morals, the values? Shouldn't we aspire to be ethical and compassionate leaders who care about the impact on others?

As leaders we have a choice in how we use our leadership skills. We have a choice in the end results of our leadership practice. A perfect example for this is *The Force* from Star

Wars movies. As we know, The Force can be used for good or evil, Jedi or Sith. It's the same power. It's the same skills. It's the same process. The difference is how the power is used and the results it brings. The Force in Star Wars can be used for good or evil. So can leadership. Our history books are filled with the stories of successful leaders who led others to do awful, immoral, and unethical things. They were leaders, but they were not compassionate leaders.

The Compassion Element of Leadership is perfectly aligned to the fourth chakra of yoga, known as the heart chakra, which concentrates on love, compassion, empathy, acceptance, and understanding for others. This element allows for our leadership actions to be moral, ethical, just, and compassionate. For example, a leader using the Compassion Element would not hire people to do a job for $1 an hour just so the profit is bigger in the end. You can't cut corners or cheat or trample others' rights or values to get to the end. It's about taking the ethical and moral path.

In the Compassion Element of Leadership, we are also thinking about the impact of our leadership. It takes into account the concepts of servant leadership and ethical leadership. What is the environment where we are leading? What are we trying to accomplish in this mission? Are we acting in a compassionate and caring way? Do we do things for others that aren't just about profit? Do we make a difference in other people's lives? Are we treating followers and employees well? Are we giving back to our community in some manner? Is our work environment healthy and happy? These things *should* matter. It shouldn't be all about financial success, it should be about way more than that.

The Compassion Element Leader cares about people and about the world around them. They care about the impact of their leadership as much as the outcomes of their leadership. Wouldn't you want to follow a leader like that? Wouldn't you want to be this type of leader? It definitely seems that Miguel is getting his Compassion Element of Leadership energized to make huge ripples in the world…

In the months that followed, Miguel continued to surprise people with his actions and his words. He found himself a regular in Lea's yoga sessions. He was finding time in his schedule to be healthy and happy and he was expecting his employees to do the same. One morning he found himself in another of Lea's sessions. He went through his favorites – the Cobra, Fish, and Warrior One Poses – and after class had wrapped up, he went up to Lea. As always, she smiled at him and asked how he was doing. Miguel smiled brightly and said, "Lea, I just wanted to say thank you for the positive impact you've had on my life. I am a different man today because of you. You have shown me a whole new world. It's a world I want to be a part of. It's a world I want to make a difference in. And it's all because of you."

"Thank you for the kind words Miguel, but you're wrong," said Lea. Miguel was surprised by the response. Lea smiled and put her palm against his heart, "The person that made the difference in your life is you. You changed your world. You changed your life. You are who you are because you took that first step out of your car and into a new life so many months ago. Remember who you are. Make your life count. Breathe out love, kindness, and compassion."

Miguel found himself tearing up yet again. That women knew just how to tug at his emotional heartstrings. He smiled through the tears as he hugged Lea and then left the studio. He couldn't stay because he had somewhere to be. It was a big day and he didn't want to be late to a very important meeting he had planned. He drove quickly over into the old rundown neighborhood where he had grown up. As he pulled up to his family's old house, which lay vacant at that time, he saw the others were already there and ready for the meeting. He smiled because those others who he was meeting with that morning were his dad and siblings.

As he got out of the car, Miguel's brother called out, "What are we doing back here Miguel? A little trip down memory lane or something?" Miguel laughed and nodded his head, "Something like that little bro. I have some news to share. As you know, years ago I bought our old property and all the other houses on our side of the street. For a long time, I didn't know what to do with all of it. But I knew I didn't want to let it go. But now I know exactly what to do. We are standing on the future home of this neighborhood's first ever community center. My company is building the entire facility and then donating it to the community. It's going to have everything that can help people and lift up this neighborhood. And I'm going to name it after our mother... the Maria Guadalupe Cardoso Community Center."

Miguel began to cry uncontrollably. It was that damn soft side he had been so afraid of for so long. But he was okay with the tears now, because it was okay to have emotions. His family came over to him and they all joined in a big family hug. Miguel's dad leaned in at Miguel's shoulder and whispered, "Your mother would be so proud of you son. I am so proud of you. We are all so proud of you."

Make my life count.
Breathe out love, kindness, and compassion.

The Charisma Element

As a teacher, Shantel had spent her entire career trying to help her students achieve all that so many people had told them wasn't possible. The stats were against her kids. They came from an at-risk neighborhood. They were trapped by societal controls. They were a part of a low socio-economic environment. They were talked about as "those kids" or from "that neighborhood" and not in the positive way that you would hope. It seemed at times that the world had given up on helping those who most needed its support.

Shantel was an outstanding teacher, having won awards for her teaching and having been recognized in front of the school board for her achievements. But the awards were nothing compared to the look on her students' faces when they would solve a problem they couldn't figure out. The awards were nothing compared to the dance kids did when they read a book that had been way too hard for them only a few weeks before. The awards were nothing compared to the hugs from students as they left her class to move onto the next grade level. The awards were nothing compared to the thank you letters she received from her former students upon their graduation from high school or even college.

This was why Shantel did what she did. This is why she turned down offers to move to other schools in more affluent parts of her school district. She had gone into teaching to make a difference and this school was where she could do just that. It's not that she couldn't have made a difference for any kid, but there was a special draw for her to this school and these kids. It was because she had been one of *these kids*. She had been from *that neighborhood*.

Throughout her career Shantel had focused on *her* classroom and *her* students. She knew she couldn't change the entire school system. She knew she couldn't control what happened anywhere else. Too many politics. Too much governance. Too much standardization. Too much influence. With all that going against education, how could it possibly change for the better on a grand scale? But Shantel, as with so many other teachers, knew she could change it on her small scale. She centered herself on what she could control in her classroom. She focused on her projects, her assignments, and her learning environment. It had allowed her to always get the most out of her kids.

Shantel was a lifelong learner, which was a bonus for her students and their families. She was constantly searching through YouTube, Pinterest, Facebook, and websites for ways she could improve her instruction and learning environment. She had learned years before not to wait for her school or district to come up with a professional development plan for teachers. She had seen every change come and go, a never-ending cycle of highly paid workshop presenters or new curriculums. The problem was that all of it was so static and robotic. The latest one called for teachers to all be on the exact same page every day. The same lessons. The same books. The same activities. The same homework. The same tests. She understood why they were pushing for this so that every child received an equal learning experience.

But over the years seeing each new concept get introduced, Shantel knew that eventually it would go away as some new idea was brought in that would *now* change the world of education. She had taught straight through dozens of these supposed world-changing concepts. Each did very little more than the one before. After several cycles of this type of change, Shantel had put all of it aside. She focused on what she knew would help kids. She would take new ideas and concepts that worked from each new cycle, but she always did her own thing. And why break the cycle, because year after year her students outperformed students in other classes. Why stop something that was working?

Some might think she was just an old fuddy-duddy teacher who was stuck in her ways and refused to change. But this couldn't have been further from the truth. She was an innovator. She was a change maker. She was a difference maker. She was always bringing in new ideas, concepts, activities, and lessons. She wasn't stuck at all in old ways, it was that she believed strongly in herself and her abilities. She didn't want to be pulled back down to the equal mean that standardized learning forced on schools. She wanted her students to excel, not just meet the average. But her ways were not always met with great fanfare, despite the awards she had won. Over the years she had been called a rebel, a rule breaker, a non-conformist. She was branded as the difficult teacher because she refused to do things like everyone else. They tried to force her to be like everyone else. They tried to force her to fit in. They tried to fix her.

But fitting in wasn't in Shantel's nature. She *was* a maverick. She *was* a rebel. She *was* a rule breaker. She *was* a non-conformist. But she saw all those things as positives for her kids. Because she knew that doing things differently meant her kids were getting opportunities that other kids weren't. She was comfortable and confident in being who she was. She believed in herself. She always had. Years before when she was a brand-new teacher, she felt the pressure to change and to fit in. She needed to keep her job. She wanted to make people happy, particularly her administrators. But she wasn't happy trying to do that. She felt trapped and held down. She was struggling emotionally and physically and even thought of leaving teaching. Maybe it just wasn't her thing. But it was at that time that her mentor, Mrs. Kitka, an old teacher who had actually taught Shantel as a child in that same school, took her under her wing.

Mrs. Kitka had been one of the greatest influences on Shantel's life as a little girl. Mrs. Kitka had taught her students to stand up for themselves and what they believed in. When Shantel started teaching at the school, she immediately got in under Mrs. Kitka's wing to learn how to be the best teacher she could. The greatest learning though took place outside of the classroom. Mrs. Kitka introduced Shantel to the practice of yoga and meditation. Mrs. Kitka believed in the way that being mindful could positively impact a person's life. Shantel had grown to love the way in which her yoga practice could bring her out of any funk she had gotten into at work. It was a way to reset her life, reignite her passion, and find herself if she was lost. The mindfulness brought on through yoga was the foundation for the difference she made with students.

For many people, yoga is about getting in a good workout, becoming more flexible, or working the muscles and joints out for greater health. You see yoga workout programs all over the place now, in gyms and studios, and all over the internet. There is nothing wrong with using yoga to get and be healthy. It can do so much for our physical wellness. So many of us need this type of exercise routine as an alternative to the high intensity cardio workouts and running regiments.

But what about our emotional wellness? What about our stress? What about our minds? What about our feelings? That's what is so amazing about yoga, because it was originally intended to focus in on the emotional and spiritual side of our beings. The spiritual side isn't about religion or religious practices, but rather about our mindfulness and connectivity to the world we live in. Do not leave behind the opportunity to be mindful, to connect with your breath, and to become one with your mind, body, and heart.

Shantel is using her yoga practice to not only be a physically healthy person, but an emotionally healthy person as well. Just like Shantel, we all deal with issues in our daily lives. It doesn't matter whether our day is filled with work, or raising kids, or going to school, we tend to be fried by the end of the day. When we get this way, we make poor decisions, we are quick to anger, we get depressed, and we don't feel good. Shantel has found her yoga practice to be a way to rejuvenate at the end of the workday. This works for her, but it may not work for you. Everyone's schedule is different, but what isn't different is our need to rejuvenate every single day. Yes, you heard that right. Every single day. We have to find time to reconnect with our inner selves. We have to find time in our daily lives to reflect and think about where we are at and where we want to go. We have to find time in our daily lives to move forward and not be stuck in the past.

And to do this, it doesn't mean you have to go to a formal yoga class. It doesn't mean you have to set aside an entire hour of your afternoon or evening to accomplish the rejuvenation. Because when we think about setting aside an entire hour (or more for some of our workouts), we tend to say, "I don't have time today, I'll get to it tomorrow." That statement is uttered over and over again until we realize we feel like crap, we're overwhelmed, we're stressed, we're sick and rundown, and we haven't rejuvenated in weeks or even months. So, then we kick back into it, but it's just about recovery from pain and illness and depression at that point. Wouldn't be better to focus on prevention? So, find the time. Start with only five minutes each day the first week. Stop yourself, sit down into Easy Pose and close your eyes. Reflect and rejuvenate. It will make a difference in your life.

This school year seemed more frustrating than any other of Shantel's career. A new principal, Ms. Cantill, had taken over at the school and was definitely putting her thumbprint on everything. She loved the standardization of education. She saw herself as the savior to a school that had for so long fallen short on standardized testing. She wanted to make a name for herself. The school had seen plenty of new young principals come through the school. It was because, as with many schools across the nation in low socio-economic neighborhoods, the school was seen as a stepping-stone into a better school. Principals and teachers cut their teeth at the school and if they could prove themselves there, then they got moved out into other more affluent schools.

The revolving door of principals who came through the school was another reason why Shantel had always kept doing her own thing in her classroom. Most of the principals over the years had left her alone because they could see she was a great teacher. Instead, they focused their attention on other teachers who they didn't think we're doing as well. But for whatever reason, Ms. Cantill was forcing change on everybody, including Shantel. Everything was handed down to them from Ms. Cantill who thought she knew everything. And the changes she was forcing were not great for teachers and more importantly not great for kids.

Everything was supposed to be structured. Everything was supposed to be out of the textbook. Tests were expected to be given every week in every subject so that the data could be tracked. All teachers were supposed to stick to a blueprint of lesson plans that were handed to the teachers without any of their input. All that could be taught was what would be on the national standardized tests. That meant double blocks of English and Math, because all that mattered were those test scores. Everything was cold and static and boring. It wasn't what kids needed. It wouldn't make them successful.

In particular, Ms. Cantill zeroed in on Shantel. She spent a lot of time in Shantel's classroom and would leave notes for her in her mailbox about the things Shantel was doing that weren't on the school-wide lesson plans for that day. It was going to be Ms. Cantill's way or the highway. But every time the principal would show up in her room, Shantel would just keep teaching the way she always did.

A few weeks into the school year, Shantel got called in for an after-school meeting with Ms. Cantill. After she had helped her last student find her bus to go home, Shantel went back to her classroom. She had ten minutes before the meeting would start and she had to get prepared. As opposed to other teachers who might have started looking at notes and lesson plans to know what to talk about with the principal, Shantel instead pulled out her yoga mat. She kicked off her shoes and she sat down and crossed her legs on the mat. She then worked her neck around, first looking down at the mat and feeling the stretch in her spine. She then arched her head back and could feel the stretch in her throat. She took her right arm and brought it up alongside her face before leaning out to her left with her arm coming over her head. She could feel the good stretch in her right side before she switched to her left side.

When Shantel walked into the principal's office for the meeting, she felt like a kid who had just been busted for getting into a fight. But regardless of how she felt, she put on a smile and walked in confidently. The meeting was not exactly friendly. Ms. Cantill was flexing every administrative muscle she could. She wanted to put Shantel in her place and let her know who the boss was on the campus.

Shantel was surprised because she didn't know what she had done to elicit such a response from the principal. Shantel had focused on her own room and stayed out of any fray. The attack by the principal seemed unwarranted. Shantel hadn't done anything to deserve this meeting. But Ms. Cantill went off about how Shantel's ways were going to have to change. She used terms like, "You're going to get with the program here," and "I'm not going to have some rebel doing her own thing," and "You aren't going to be a bad influence on everyone who is doing things the way I want them done." Shantel was shocked by the way in which Ms. Cantill was referring to her. She definitely was not a rabble rouser, and she didn't want to influence anyone to do anything. She had never tried to get others to be like her or teach like her. She just wanted to be left alone to do her own thing.

Shantel tried to mentally leave the room because she hated what she was hearing. She was becoming angry at the way in which she was being treated. She didn't like to be angry or frustrated. She tried to think of her yoga and meditation. She tried to think about being in a yoga class and feeling the positivity. But with every word Ms. Cantill said, Shantel could feel her neck and shoulders tightening up. The tension and the pain were setting in. She could feel a lump coming up in her throat. She hadn't felt this way in a very long time. It only got worse when Ms. Cantill said, "I am going to be watching you like a hawk. You are going to get in line with the program. You are going to do things my way or I will have you transferred to another school."

Shantel couldn't believe what she had heard. She couldn't imagine being sent somewhere else. Then Ms. Cantill said the statement that was the last straw for Shantel, "All of these teachers keep telling me how great you are and how you are the best teacher they've ever seen. But what I've seen doesn't impress me at all and they shouldn't be following what you do. I'm going to fix these teachers and these kids and you're not going to get in my way." Shantel shut down with that statement. Another all-knowing savior who was going to fix everyone in the school and the neighborhood.

Shantel was an absolute mess when she left the meeting. There was a part of her that wanted to flee by putting in an immediate request for a transfer. How could she just follow along blindly to something that wasn't good for her kids. That wasn't who she was. That wasn't what her kids needed. But what could she do? She wasn't a principal or administrator of any kind. She was *just* a teacher. She wasn't even a department chair at her grade level. She was *just* a teacher. No one would listen to her. Even if she wanted to do something, the voice in her head was saying no...

> Do you really think you can do anything? You're just a teacher. You have no power. You have no voice. No one will listen to you. You're just a teacher.

Shantel is like so many of us who won't do something that is wrong just because someone tells us to do it. Isn't this what leadership is all about? Most of the greatest leaders in the history of the world didn't just do what everyone else did or said. If they had, then they wouldn't be leaders. Leaders affect change. They motivate others to move towards change. It can be on the small scale, such as leading the decision-making process on where a group is going to eat dinner that night. It can also be on the grand scale, such as leading the development of a new charity to support an important cause. Leadership is about change. It's about recognizing the problem a group faces, finding a solution for the problem, and then getting everyone to move forward!

How many times in your life have you faced a situation like Shantel? Where someone has said or done something to you that is offensive, or wrong, or mean. They take out their frustrations on you. Or, as in the case of Shantel and Ms. Cantill, someone is going to make an example out of you. Typically, this is because they feel threatened as is the case with Ms. Cantill. Shantel was a threat to the new principal's opportunity to be the savior. And like most inexperienced bosses, instead of finding a way to use Shantel's influence on others to work together to affect change, Ms. Cantill is going to take down the threat. When bosses see a threat to their authority, they are going to knock out the threat.

Notice how we are using the terms *boss* and *authority* rather than *leader* and *power*. This is intentional because there is a huge difference between the two sides. Bosses are always afraid of losing their authority, because it's all they have to keep their employees in line. But leaders don't necessarily have any authority, they have to find ways to keep followers wanting to follow them. In the situation that Shantel faces, her leadership has just been sparked. Before that moment, she never saw herself as a leader. She was just a teacher who kept to herself and did what she thought was best for her kids. But as Ms. Cantill noted, other teachers look up to Shantel and want to follow the way she does things.

Sometimes we don't even realize our leadership potential. Sometimes we are blind to the opportunities we have to make a difference for others. But often, it takes a moment like Shantel had with the principal to spark our potential. Moments like this generate a power within us to change something that is wrong around us. This is where leadership is born. Recognizing an issue like racism or sexism or bullying and feeling the urge inside of you to do something about it. Shantel is feeling that in this moment, but as with many new emerging leaders, she is questioning whether she can actually do it. We tell ourselves we are nobodies. We tell ourselves no one will listen. We tell ourselves we have no influence. We tell ourselves we are *just* a follower.

At the end of the week, Shantel found herself back at Lea's Life Studio for a special session that focused on the Throat Chakra. Shantel typically would do her own yoga sessions at home by herself. But at least once a week, she tried to get to Lea's because there was a different aura around the studio. It was a nice break from doing things on her own. And she always enjoyed talking with Lea before or after class. She enjoyed Lea, much like she had enjoyed working with her old mentor Mrs. Kitka. It was Mrs. Kitka who introduced Shantel to Lea and her studio. Because Shantel had been doing yoga for many years, she always made sure to try and hit up one of Lea's more advanced sessions. It always helped to push Shantel out of her comfort zone.

This session had stood out to Shantel when she looked over the schedule for the week. She instantly was drawn to this idea of a focus on the throat chakra, one that Shantel was not that familiar with. But there was something inside of her that was telling her to get to that session. Lea started out by talking to the class about their throat chakra, and how it represents a person's ability to be expressive. She talked about the blocks to having a balanced chakra, in that you often feel ignored or that you have no voice. She talked about how it all manifests in our bodies as neck, shoulder, and throat pain. How it can cause you to feel sluggish as though you have no willpower. It can feel as though you never have a voice, and everyone just seems to talk right over you. She shared a mantra that she found was super helpful in balancing the chakra. It was what she wanted them to concentrate on as they were working through the routine... My voice is mighty when I speak for those who are silenced.

Shantel smiled when she heard the words from Lea. She agreed that her inner voice was mighty when it came to her students. She knew what she was doing as a teacher. But was she really strong enough to have it heard? She had always been the quiet one. She had always been the one to keep to herself and do her own thing. She didn't want to get involved in stuff because she liked to be left alone. But now with her principal breathing down her neck, could she really just hide?

"Let's get started everybody," Lea called out to the class. They worked through several easy poses to warm up, and then Lea moved into the poses that would energize their throat chakras. The first was the Camel Pose. Shantel was familiar with this one. She moved up onto her knees and then slowly moved her hands back along her legs till they were holding onto the inside of her feet. Her stomach and chest were arched up towards the sky and her head was back out over her feet. She closed her eyes and began to focus…

My voice is mighty when I speak for those who are silenced. My voice is mighty when I speak for those who are silenced.

Shantel continued to focus in on the mantra over and over again as they moved out of the Camel Pose and into a more difficult pose… the Candle Pose. She had only done this pose a few times before, but she was up for the challenge. While lying flat on her mat, Shantel pulled her knees into her chest as she breathed out. Then she moved her hands over and placed them flat on the ground under her back. Her elbows were down on the ground as she extended her legs up slowly to where they were straight above her. She held her body up with her hands and started to focus in again…

My voice is mighty when I speak for those who are silenced. My voice is mighty when I speak for those who are silenced.

She could feel the power filling her lungs. She felt as though she was being called to do more and to be more. She was powerful. She was strong enough to take on a terrible plan that the principal was throwing down at kids and teachers. Every breath she took in the Candle Pose only filled her with more passion to speak out and be heard. Eventually the class moved into the Plough Pose which basically brought the straight legs of the Candle Pose down over her head as her toes touched the ground out in front of her head. From that pose, she felt ready to speak out loudly to the world.

As the class ended, Shantel walked by Lea who reached out and hugged her. Lea asked about how her students were doing this year. Shantel got excited. She loved to talk about her kids because she was proud of them. She was proud of the work she did with them. She said to Lea, "They're doing great. A good group of little ones this year. By the way, I've got something to show you on my phone!"

With that Shantel pulled out her phone and flipped to her photos. She held up the phone to Lea who started giggling at the sight. There was Shantel's entire 3rd grade class standing by their desks doing the Eagle Pose. She flipped through several other photos showing them doing various other standing poses including Tree, Warrior, and Mountain. Shantel shared, "For safety reasons, we can't do anything too difficult or that involves getting down on the ground, but I've found that the kids love the yoga and it calms them down and focuses them so much. It's so cool to see."

Lea smiled and told Shantel how great it was to see her using yoga with the kids. Shantel smiled and said, "It's great, but I realized this week that I need to do more than just help my own kids. I need to let my voice help every kid and teacher in the school. I want to do more and to help more." Lea smiled again and said, "I agree Shantel. You are strong. You are powerful. You are smart. Your voice needs to be heard. And when you doubt yourself, because there will be times where you doubt your voice, look at those pics again so you are reminded why you need to be heard."

To be a great leader, you don't have to be a great speaker or have a great public voice. But you do have to be able to inspire and motivate others to do great things. Some people can do this through their speaking, stirring up emotions inside of others that make them want to make a difference.

Think Martin Luther King, Jr. here and his ability to speak to huge crowds. But other leaders do this by example and through modeling what it is that others should be doing. Think Mother Theresa here and the way in which she influenced people to want to do more for others without saying a single word. There are many ways to get people to move forward, but the key here is that there has to be a vision of where they all want to go. That's what Lea is talking about in terms of not losing sight of what you are focused on as a leader. The reason for change is paramount.

Put yourself in the shoes of one of the other teachers at Shantel's school. If she was to speak up and talk about how things need to change and it's all because the principal personally treated her poorly, would you necessarily follow her? Some of you might if you connect with Shantel and her story, or if you've shared a similar experience. But let's say you happen to have had your own issues with Shantel in the past. Are you going to follow her ideas for change? Probably not. But now let's say the change is not about Shantel's personal issue with the principal, but instead she says it's about what's best for kids. She shows how the curriculum and instructional ideas are negatively affecting kids. Now would you jump on board with change? The answer is yes.

So, the difference here isn't the leader, for Shantel would be the leader in both situations. The difference is the vision and the reason for the change. That's why it's so important for a leader, particularly a leader working within the **Charisma Element of Leadership**, to figure out what the actual vision is for the change. This doesn't have to be a solo project for the leader, but rather it can be built through conversations between leaders and followers. The key is figuring out what's at stake, what it's affecting, what change could look like, and then motivating others to be a part of the change process.

In this Element of Leadership, the key is figuring out how to use your voice (or actions) to inspire others to do great things. Yes, we mean great things. It's one thing to lead at the small level in terms of leading the decision as to what movie to go see... but, it's a whole other story when it comes to the big leadership dilemmas that exist in the world. Shantel is facing one of those right now with her school. The principal is not motivating anyone to want to be a part of the change. What if her change idea was actually great (it's not in this case, but let's pretend), and she still took the same approach of forcing them to do it? It doesn't matter how great the idea is because people don't want another boss in their lives. They want a leader. They want, as the old book series says... *to choose their own adventure.*

The next week Shantel found herself in the lunchroom surrounded by her fellow teachers. The conversation turned to discussing the new principal and her brutal reign as boss. Teachers were complaining about the new rules and expectations and how they were taking the joy out of their teaching. They talked about the negative impact they could see taking hold of their kids. They were already sick of the professional development provided by the principal that focused on scripted teaching straight from the textbook. It was so boring. So dull. So stupid. This was not the way to reach children and they knew it. After a few minutes, one of the younger teachers spoke up, "Shantel, I would love to hear what you think of all of this?"

Up until that point, Shantel had remained quiet on the situation. She looked at the teacher, then turned to look around the table. All the teachers had stopped eating and were looking right at her. This was her moment. This is where a leader steps up and takes up the torch of change. This was a group that wanted change but needed the right person to get them going. Shantel pursed her lips, preparing to speak, but her mouth was dry. The doubts came pouring into her head. She closed her eyes and breathed in deeply trying to find composure. But the doubts were still there...

Why me? Can't one of them take this up? Who would listen to me? I'm just a teacher. I don't get mixed up in stuff like this. I take care of myself. That's the way it's always been. Keep quiet and stay in your room where no one can bother you. You aren't cut out for leadership. You're just a teacher. Why would anyone look to you? Why would anyone follow you?

"Earth to Shantel!!! Are you there? Hey Shantel, you ok?" another teacher jokingly yelled out. Shantel looked up as she realized she was zoning out, totally lost in her own doubts. She grabbed her bottle of water and took a sip...

My voice is mighty when I speak for those who are silenced. My voice is mighty when I speak for those who are silenced. My voice is mighty when I speak for those who are silenced.

"Here's what I think about the situation. It's total crap. It's terrible for kids. It's terrible for teachers. It crushes our creativity. It kills our innovation. It destroys the fun in our classroom. It forces kids to only learn two subjects in a single solitary way. What's being lost is the whole child in this plan. What's being lost is the fact that I can teach Math and English out in nature or in a project better than reading from a script in a textbook." Shantel looked around the room and saw every teacher looking at her. No one was upset. Then Shantel remembered what Lea had said about focus.

"The worst part of this whole situation is that the kids... our kids, are going to suffer. And how do we know that? Because we are strong, smart teachers who know what we are doing."

The room erupted in cheers and clapping. One of the teachers asked Shantel what they should do about it. Shantel smiled. It was time to lead. It was time to have her voice heard, not because she needed power or attention, but because the kids she cared so much about needed help.

"I don't have all the answers. Each of you don't have all the answers. But I know that if you get all of us teachers in a room figuring out the answers... we can change the world. It's all about what is best for kids and I don't know about you, but I would do anything to make sure they succeed in life. If you want to be a part of it then come by my room tomorrow after school and let's figure it out together." It felt goofy as she said it... this idea they were going to change the world... but as she looked around the room, everyone was smiling and energized. They started all talking at the same time. People were thanking Shantel. They were talking up ideas for things they could do differently. The entire room was buzzing with energy... and the coolest part of it was that it was the best kind of energy... it was change energy.

The next afternoon, the bell rang to end the school day. Shantel and the other teachers went out to the parking lot and helped kids get to their buses and to their parents' cars. After all the kids were picked up, Shantel returned to her room wondering if anyone was going to actually show up. Everyone seemed to like the idea in the lunchroom, but would they still like it the next day? Shantel went back into her room and stood next to her desk. She slowly moved her body into the Mountain Pose. It felt good to release the stress. She moved into her Eagle Pose. She could feel the strength of her voice rising up inside her. But no one was there. No one was coming. She thought about her voice and her leadership. Just then she heard her door creak open and when she looked up, she saw a stream of teachers come filing into the room. They were excitedly talking and happy as could be. It was the first time in several weeks that she had seen anyone smiling on campus.

The next couple of hours were a whirlwind. Shantel and the other teachers all sat at student desks talking and sharing ideas about things they could do differently in their teaching. Some of the teachers asked Shantel to show them a couple of her instructional practices that they wanted to learn more about. At other times, other teachers would stand up and walk their colleagues through ideas and things they did with their kids. The room was a think lab. It was a place of innovation. No one was worried about a curriculum or a textbook or a stupid script. They were talking about ways in which they could bring learning to life. Ways that they could work around the system. At the end of the session, Shantel spoke to the whole group. She thanked them all for being there and for being a part of this change process. Then she left them with a mantra that might help them to continue moving forward even when Ms. Cantill would come after them. The words she wanted them to remember were…

**My voice is mighty when I speak
for those who are silenced.**

When we think of leadership, we often visualize the big public speech in front of a huge crowd. It's moving and inspirational and it is BIG!!! But so much of the leadership we experience on a daily basis doesn't happen on a big stage. It doesn't happen with a microphone in front of us. It doesn't happen with a huge crowd. All change starts at the small level. Sometimes it catches fire and spreads to the large scale. But whether or not it goes huge, leadership exists in our daily actions. We all have the potential to be a leader. We all have the potential to do leadership. But often the hardest part is finding the *voice* inside of us to actually lead.

A lot of this is based on fear. Leaders face a lot of criticism from outside of the group of followers. Sometimes they face criticism from within the group. They are often the face of a change movement and so all the critical arrows are flying their way as if they are holding a giant, football field sized bullseye. It causes some to fear taking on leadership. They don't believe in themselves. They wait for someone else to take the lead. This is often the case in break rooms and lunchrooms and in bars after work. Everyone loves to complain and whine. But rare are the ones like Shantel who find the voice to step up and get the change process started.

Many people think that leaders must always be in the front. They think leaders must come up with every idea. They think leaders have to make every decision. They think leaders have to always lead. But all of these are just myths we tell ourselves to block ourselves from realizing our leadership potential. As with this situation, Shantel answered the call for leadership in that lunchroom. It did not mean she had to lead the entire time. During the meeting in her classroom the next day, she sat right alongside her fellow teachers, with the group, not out in front in some power position.

Think about the old legends of King Arthur and the Knights of the Round Table. The round table wasn't some kind of Feng Shui thing. It wasn't as though Sir Gawain went all Joanna Gaines and thought a round table fit better in the space. It was about the notion that all the people at the table were equals. At different times, different knights could take the role of leader. No one was relying on one single person to lead all the time. This is what made their team so strong. For these teachers, it's the same idea. All of them are taking on leadership in this change process. All of them are involved in the vision. All of them are involved in the solution. This makes their change process strong, because no matter what happens to any single one of them (if the principal sends Shantel to another school), the change can continue. This is power. This is change. This is leadership.

This is what the Charisma Element of Leadership is all about. It is aligned to the fifth chakra, known as the throat or sound chakra, which concentrates on authentic communication, speaking truthfully, and self-expression. The main concept in this element of leadership is the focus on the ability of a leader to motivate and inspire their followers to make change. While most people focus on the ability to speak publicly with great passion and energy (think Martin Luther King, Jr. or Oprah or Churchill or JFK), speaking publicly is not the only way to energize your Charisma Element of Leadership. Charismatic leaders all do one thing really well – they connect followers with the cause through emotions. They make you feel something. They make you care about something. Think of the high school football coach who fires up the locker room with a rousing speech, after which the team charges out onto the field ripping through the big banner to start the game. That is the visual image of a charismatic leader.

But you don't have to rouse everybody up with some pump-up speech in the locker room. What you have to do to work within the Charisma Element of Leadership is to get people to deeply connect with the cause. To feel something. To be emotionally connected – whether it's tears, or anger, or excitement. And then you want them to do something about the situation. That's charisma. That's leadership.

Over the course of the next few months, the change really took over the school. Shantel and the other teachers began meeting two days a week to talk through new ideas of how to work around the forced lesson plans, scripting, and curriculum. They made modifications, innovations, and changes to everything. They added in new ideas, activities, projects, and practices to their classroom. They shared ideas, and teachers took turns teaching their peers. Despite the principal continuing to push her agenda in staff meetings, emails, and conferences with teachers, the staff was not deterred. They continued to focus in on the vision that was success for all students, not just in school, but in overall life. They thought about the whole child and not just what would show up on a standardized test. There was happiness and excitement again in classrooms and hallways.

Shantel had continued to work on her yoga practice by herself, with her students, and even with some of the other teachers. She now had a small core group of teachers that would go with her to Lea's Life Studio. During this time,

Shantel had particularly been focused on developing her throat chakra because it was what she needed most to energize as a leader. She felt so in balance. She was not deterred even when Ms. Cantill would call her into the office.

Ms. Cantill could tell something was going on with the staff and she kept coming after Shantel to try to figure out what it was. Ms. Cantill was frustrated that the changes she wanted to see happen were not taking place. Her threats to teachers to mark their evaluations down for not following directions had not stopped them from teaching their own way. Every time she would go into a classroom, she would see textbooks out on desks, but the teachers were never using them.

The worst part about it for Ms. Cantill was that she started hearing from teachers that they were loving their teaching and that their kids were doing great. She was also hearing from parents of kids in the school how impressed they were with what was happening at the school. The data backed it up. Despite not teaching the way Ms. Cantill wanted them to, the test score data was showing improvement across the board. It wasn't like every kid was now in the highest scoring group of all test takers in the country, but in every category, kids were doing better than they had in previous years.

Ms. Cantill called Shantel in to talk again. On her desk Ms. Cantill had all the test score data. Whereas the first time

Shantel had gone into the room, she felt like she was getting in trouble, this time Shantel walked in tall and proud. She knew their work was making a difference. She just kept repeating the new mantra for her life...

> My voice is mighty when I speak for those who are silenced. My voice is mighty when I speak for those who are silenced.

Ms. Cantill started talking to her about how she wasn't happy with what was going on in the school. She shared that she didn't like being undermined by Shantel. She said she knew Shantel was behind this whole movement and she wanted it to stop. Shantel didn't trip over her words at all in this case as she said, "So let me get this straight. You're upset that students are doing better in school. You're upset that parents are happy with the progress their children are making. You're upset that teachers have found their love and passion for teaching again. You're upset that our school is bucking every trend in education. If you're upset about these things, then I'm not sure why you're in education."

Ms. Cantill seemed shocked by the response. In truth, Shantel was a little shocked she had actually said what she said. She thought about how months ago she would have just sat quietly and listened. But through her yoga practice, she now felt empowered to have her voice heard. Ms. Cantill stammered and stumbled with her words, not really knowing how to respond, but did get out a single statement, "No. I'm not against any of those things…"

Shantel smiled with pride. She looked at the principal and stated things as clearly as she could, "This train is moving forward, and it's moving fast. We are going somewhere and everybody on this campus is on board. Every teacher, every student, every parent. The only person not on board is you! My advice would be to jump on board or get left behind. But know that your ticket to ride this train is at will call waiting for you to pick up. I really hope you'll join us on this journey to make a difference for kids." Shantel stood up and left the room with Ms. Cantill sitting in complete and utter silence.

Later that afternoon, Shantel's room was on fire with excitement as another session of their change meeting was going on. They had even named the room *The Change Lab* and had hung a sign with the name on the door every afternoon they had a session. Everybody in the room was talking and sharing when they heard the door open. In through the doors stepped the last person they thought they would ever see… Ms. Cantill.

The room went dead quiet in fear. Ms. Cantill walked in sheepishly. Everyone was staring at her not knowing what to do. Ms. Cantill looked around the room and said, "Please carry on, I'm here to learn and listen. I want to join the team.

I hope it's okay that I'm here?" The teachers looked around at each other not quite knowing how to respond. The room was frozen. The room was dead quiet.

Shantel stood up from her seat and walked over to where Ms. Cantill stood. Shantel was channeling her inner-Lea in that moment. She reached out with open arms and took the principal into her arms in a hug. "Welcome to The Change Lab! Anyone who wants to make a difference in kids' lives is always welcome here. We are so happy you joined us!" The principal began to cry into Shantel's shoulder as the entire room erupted in cheers and excitement. The train was leaving the station and now *everybody* was on board. And to think it was all because one woman who was *just* a teacher found her voice…

**My voice is mighty when I speak
for those who are silenced.**

The Authentic Element

As she sat at her desk, Rebecca could feel the headache coming on. Her vision was blurry, and her temples were starting to really hurt. The headaches seemed to be happening more often than ever lately. And now she was starting to have vision issues as well. She had tried everything to curb the problems. She had been to the eye doctor to get new glasses since she spent so much time in front of computers. She had tried working without the lights on in her office because she had heard that fluorescent lights could cause issues. She had tried drinking more water to keep her system fully hydrated. But they did little to curb the issues. The only thing Rebecca had found that helped was to close her eyes and go through a short meditation time.

She had learned this technique in her yoga sessions at Lea's Yoga Studio. She loved yoga and would have gone more often if it weren't for her busy schedule. She saw yoga as a way to destress. Every session was an opportunity to reflect on her life and to reconnect herself with who she really was. But this had been a struggle she had been dealing with for a while. She had told herself you don't make it to this position without having to sacrifice a little bit. But lately she felt like she was sacrificing so much of herself, maybe all of herself. It was overwhelming to try to think about it all. And that pain in her head just kept getting worse. She reached for her water bottle and took a swig of it. Then she leaned back in her chair and rolled her shoulders back. She lowered her chin down towards her chest and closed her eyes…

Slow down. Take a breath. Another breath. Another breath. Slow down. This pain is nothing. It will go away. What is bothering me the most right now? I don't want to be here right now. I want to go home… or maybe to a yoga session. I'm tired. I'm grumpy. I'm upset. I need a day off. The weekend can't get here fast enough. But even if comes, will I actually take the time off? Will I really not work? Yeah right, I'll be slammed and have to work the entire time. Wait. Stop. Don't talk bad to myself. What does Lea always say? Oh yeah. Be positive. Think positive. Talk positive. Just breathe Rebecca…

A knock at her door stopped her thoughts. "Rebecca, is this a bad time?" She opened her eyes to see her friend Farrah at the door. Rebecca laughed and replied, "Is it ever really a good time? What's up Farrah?" Farrah apologetically continued, "Sorry Rebecca, I didn't mean to interrupt your quiet time." Rebecca brought a little smile to her lips so as to not make her head hurt worse, "No worries. I was just hoping a little meditation might knock this headache out." Farrah smiled sympathetically, "Well I wouldn't interrupt if we didn't need you for that meeting with Mrs. Wilson. Remember the complaint she lodged this week? We were supposed to meet with her today to talk it through."

Rebecca nodded her head letting Farrah know she knew about the meeting. She scooped up Mrs. Wilson's file and her pen and walked out of the room with Farrah. This was her life. Meeting after meeting. File after file. Report after report. It was an endless cycle. But what did she expect, she was the human resources manager for a major corporation. The endless meetings, files, and reports came with the job. She knew that going in. She knew that the whole time as she was working her way up to land this top job.

What she hadn't quite realized many years before when she started her journey to a leadership role in human resources, was that the job also came with incredible stress, long hours, feeling overwhelmed, and a never-ending repetition of headaches. Yeah, they had forgotten to write that up in the job description. Then again it wasn't like she didn't know about the long hours and the stress as she was working her way up the corporate ladder. But back then she was young, single, eager, motivated, focused, and everything else a twenty-something is armed with as they start out. But now she was a forty-year-old. She was married. She had kids. She had other things in life than work that sought her time and energy. She was tired. She was stressed. She was living on way too much coffee and way too little sleep.

And the worst thing about it all was that she was starting to really think she was depressed. She shouldn't have been. At least that's what everyone always told her. She had it all. Family. Loved ones. A great job. A great salary. She made a difference with her work by standing up for so many people who had been treated poorly or had dealt with sexism or racism or ageism. She was the voice for all the people who needed help. But everyone that Rebecca tried to talk to about how she was really feeling about life, just didn't understand her. No one was sympathetic. No one was empathetic. They just didn't understand why she was so down all the time. Her parents had taught her as a child to talk to people when she was feeling bad, but it seemed that every person she talked to just made it worse. Her husband didn't get it at all and told her she should be happy. Her friends never wanted to hear her complain because their issues were so much bigger than the problems Rebecca was having (or so they said).

Out of options and wanting a place to vent, she had even started seeing a therapist. But she found these sessions difficult because she felt that she was always being judged. The therapist swore that she wasn't there to judge, but rather to help Rebecca find solutions, but Rebecca just wasn't feeling it. Half the time when she left a therapy session, Rebecca felt worse about herself than when she went into the session. She had nowhere to turn and so she just kept internalizing the issues she was having. The sickening cycle of depression was starting to really set in...

One of the most difficult aspects of life is to find people to talk to who really truly understand who we are. This is increasingly more difficult as we move further ahead in life. We find tons of similarities with others at our younger ages because we are sharing so many of the same experiences. When we are starting college or starting a job out of high school, we are all going through the same trying times. Whether it's finding love or trying to get the same assignment done in a class or finding a good healthy option at the dining hall buffet, we can all kibitz about the same things. It helps that we are typically living with our friends either in a dorm room or a shared apartment. But as we grow, we lose the connections we used to find so easily.

It's because our paths are apt to veer away from each other. Different paths for different folks. Different jobs, different homes, different lives. As we venture further apart from old friends, we feel ever more isolated and alone. It's not like we won't find new people to hang with, such as friends at work or people in the new building we move to or a special someone we fall in love with. But it's never quite the same.

While there are so many positives to growing up and developing throughout our lives (obviously way better than staying the same as we were in college for ever) there are negatives that come with it. One of the biggest issues we face at each new step is what Rebecca is dealing with. We become less connected with each new group along our life path. Each new step seems to bring less understanding from the social groups that we find ourselves in. We become hyper aware that our complaining might come across the wrong way to someone else who isn't going through the same thing.

Think back to your younger years when you were on the dating market, trying to find that special someone. If you got stood up on a date by some complete jerk, you have no problem sharing it with someone else in your social circle because it's guaranteed half, if not all, of the people in the group have had something similar happen to them. Now move ahead a few years and you've found that special loved one. Now you go to that same group of friends and complain how your loved one no longer buys you gifts on your anniversary. As you are complaining about this you realize that three of your friends haven't found love yet. You suddenly become aware that what you're complaining about is going to sound awful to them because all they want is to find someone to love, but they're still stuck in single player mode. Move ahead further and start complaining about your kids and see how the group reacts when several of them haven't been able to have kids yet. You start feeling like a real jerk... oh yeah, and all alone.

The same goes with our career path. Think about the nurse who's been promoted to shift leader in the maternity ward at the local hospital. She had been a nurse there for ten years and was so connected to all her fellow nurses. They would socialize after work at the local watering hole and swap stories about life over coffee in the mornings. But now that she's been promoted to managing her fellow nurses (a position she has been working hard to move up to), she suddenly finds the dynamic in the group has changed. She doesn't get invited for the beer or even the coffee. No one shares their stories with her. When she walks up to a small group of her old friends to join in, they scurry and get back to work. The dynamic is no longer of equals and similarities, but rather now about boss/employee and differences.

While she has achieved a great position (and a better salary), she is suddenly seen as *other* to her friends because now she is in management. Her path had veered away from her friends, which left her isolated, alone, and with no one to talk to about the issues she was struggling with in the new role. Of all times when she needed people the most (because of the change), she has no one to turn to. Her old nursing friends don't get it because they aren't in management and she barely knows any of the other shift leaders so she can't turn to them. She is stuck in a chasm with no bridge.

It's what Rebecca is dealing with. Who do you turn to? Who do you talk to? Who understands you? Often, we think there is no one there for us so we begin to internalize every issue we're having. We shut ourselves down and become consumed by negative talk. We become consumed by worrying about what others think of us because we feel separated. We become disconnected from the world around us and get stuck in a depressed state of being.

The meeting with Mrs. Wilson ran long, as all these meetings always did. How could you stop a person with a time boundary when they're pouring their heart out about a situation where they felt wronged. It wasn't like Rebecca could set a timer and let it beep and then walk out of the room mid-story. How would that make the person feel who had stepped forward and was trying to voice what they were experiencing? Rebecca cared too much about the people she worked with. She cared too much about the company and making sure the situation was handled appropriately.

It was now an hour past the end of the workday, and Rebecca was just getting back to her office. She grabbed her cell phone from the drawer of her desk and touched the screen. Nine texts were showing. She didn't even want to look at them because they were always the same. Whoever it was, whether family or friends, would be asking her why she was still at work. The same question she always got. She opened the phone and called home. The conversation went as it normally did. Rebecca apologizing for working late. Her family frustrated she was still at work. When they asked her how much longer she'd be, it was the same old answer, "I have to finish up this report which will take maybe twenty minutes and then I'll head for home."

> How many times have I said this before? It's never true. As hard as I try, I know I won't be done in twenty minutes. It'll take longer because it always takes longer. And they'll be pissed. And I'll be upset. Because I'm a terrible mom and wife. They have no idea how much I have to do in this job. They have no idea how difficult it is to be sitting here. They think I don't want to be home. They think I want to be here. If only they knew the truth. I want to be there with them. But if I do that then I let down Mrs. Wilson and all the others who come to me. My life is impossible. Oh, and there it is again. The headache. This sucks...

It was an all too familiar pattern for Rebecca. A pattern she was *so* tired of. A pattern she *so* badly wanted to fix. But no matter what she did, she was going to let somebody down. It was the way it always went. If she went home on time, she was letting down her company and the people she was there to help. If she stayed at work, she was letting down her family. And then there was the whole idea of letting herself down, but she had given up on that years ago. Her own self was the least of her worries. She knew she should have been trying to find ways to care for herself, but how could she possibly do that? What would her family think if she finally got home from work and said, "Peace out, I'm going to have a drink with friends," or "Hey I'd love to hang with you all, but I really need to work out and get a yoga session in." Yeah right, that would go over really well.

And so, Rebecca just continued to drag herself through the rut that was her life. It was a rut she had become way too familiar with. All she ever thought about was what everyone around her thought about her. Every action she took she thought through all the possibilities of what her family or coworkers would think of her. Every decision was based on what it would do to the others around her. She had completely lost any attempt to actually do something for herself. That was preposterous. She wanted to. She wanted to yell out with a huge bullhorn to everybody in her life, "Give me a break. Get off my back and out of my head and let me be me. Just five minutes for me. That's all I want!" But she couldn't because everybody needed more of her.

And so, despite the headache, she got back to her job. She had to write up the report on the meeting while it was still fresh in her head. She wasn't alone as Farrah had stuck around to help her work on it. She enjoyed working with Farrah as they had a lot in common. Rebecca liked Farrah because she had been Farrah fifteen years before. Just starting out, building her career, no family yet. Nothing holding her back in her life. Farrah could put the hours in, it didn't even faze her. She could keep rolling like she had all the energy in the world. Rebecca could barely remember the last time she had even the slightest bit of energy.

Rebecca used to actually reenergize by working out. It was cardio to get her pumped up and take out some of the stress. It was yoga or Pilates to push all the negative energy out. But as each day mounted onto the previous one, she just kept missing her workouts. There was way too much else to do in her life. When she would try to do something for her own health or happiness, she would be overtaken by utter guilt.

Without working out consistently she would find herself looking in the mirror and feeling terrible about herself. She could recognize where her body had been toned and fit in years past, it was now much softer than before. She could see her sunken-in eyes from a lack of sleep. She could notice the grey hairs setting in, no matter how much her hairdresser tried to cover them up. She noticed the woman looking back at her in the mirror never ever seemed to smile. She was starting to not recognize the woman in the mirror. She hated the woman in the mirror. She was miserable.

Farrah and Rebecca finished up the report and called it a night. It was now two and a half hours after the workday was supposed to end. But like so many other people in the world, work rarely ends right at 5 pm anymore. This wasn't an old school factory with timecards being punched. As with so many businesses, you work whatever hours are needed to get the job done. Farrah took off to go out with some friends to a local bar for a bite to eat and some drinks. Rebecca, on the other hand, left for home. She knew the night would be just like the last one and the one before that and countless others before that. She would drive home feeling terrible about being late. The guilt would build up so much as she drove home that by the time she got there she would go completely into defensive mode. It was survival at that point. Any little comment from the husband or the kids would feel like an attack because she felt terrible about not being home.

She knew she would then pour herself a glass of wine and try to unwind in front of the TV while surfing social media to see what her friends were up to. This only made it worse because she would see Facebook and Instagram posts that made it seem like her friends never had to work. There were pictures of them working out, hanging out at a bar, going on a field trip with their kids, on a Hawaiian vacation, or visiting the zoo. It felt like everybody around her had everything she didn't have. Fun. Relaxation. Money. Friends. Happiness. Fitness. Hobbies. Joy. It only made her feel worse, but she couldn't help herself from checking the social media. If only she had the time to do all that other stuff. But as with most nights, she just fell asleep on the couch completely exhausted. A pile of chocolate wrappers and a half empty glass of wine on the table beside her, her phone nestled in her lap. Tomorrow would be the same as today and the same as yesterday and the day before that. This was Rebecca's life.

There is a major negative impact on our happiness, health, and wellness when we are constantly and consistently focusing on validation from others for what we should feel about ourselves. This is living outside of ourselves. It's focusing on the outer voices rather than the inner voice. Too often in our lives, we live by what others think of us. We live by what others are doing that we aren't doing. We judge ourselves based not on our own selves, but rather on what others are doing and what they are owning. We don't look inside ourselves. We look outwardly. We spend so much time listening to the voices in our lives, but we spend very little time listening to our own inner voice. We get caught up in what everyone is saying about us. We get caught up in what we think everyone around us is thinking about us. We get caught up in the messages we think the world is sending us. We become addicted to what everyone else has to say. We become addicted to the messages our social media is sending us. We get addicted to feeling bad about ourselves.

The problem is that when we focus on the outer, we often get caught up in negative self-talk. We get caught up in the negative messages the world is sending out. When we live outside of ourselves, we lose track of our inner selves. We lose track of our happiness. We lose track of our peace. We judge ourselves on everyone else around us. We say things like, "Life isn't fair," "Why can't I do that," "Why don't I have that," "Why does everything work out for her and not me," and "What is wrong with me?" This is the negative self-talk that consumes us and eats away at our happiness like termites on an old wooden shack. Devouring. Destroying.

And social media is one of the biggest predators on our happiness. It's because we're seeing what everyone else is posting as positives, which replaces our ability to see what is positive about our own lives. We lose sight of the fact that people aren't going to post about all the crap they're dealing with in life. They're going to focus on the great things, the fun days, the joy. They may have had that amazing weekend in Las Vegas that we are totally jealous of, but we're only seeing the tip of the iceberg. It looks amazing, but what if all the iceberg under the water is a mess. The problem is we never see the negative, crappy part they don't want people to know about. Meanwhile we are submerged under the water of our own lives, staring straight at the massive iceberg of our lives under the water with no ability at times to get to the surface to see the beauty of the tip.

In the 1980s, well-known psychologist Dr. Faye Crosby, wrote about what she called Relative Deprivation Theory. The theory suggests we feel injustice in our lives when we look at what others have, and we don't have. Crosby suggests that perceiving others having better than we have or more than we have (in whatever aspects of our life we focus on) causes us to feel deprived, resentful, angry, and to feel a lack of satisfaction with our own lives. It's a focus on judging our lives based on the lives of others. When we constantly look at others, we're going to feel deprived. We are going to feel less than. We're going to feel life isn't fair. But the problem is that this is caused by focusing only on the aspects of the other person where they *beat* us. Whether it's their house, their job, their money, or their vacation, we focus on that which they have better than we do. But when we get into this mode of constant comparison, we rarely focus on the areas of our lives where we may have more or be living a better life then the people around us.

We can't find happiness through the lens of what others have or what others do. There's no happiness through the lens of what others think of us or say about us. We can only find happiness by looking inward and knowing who we truly are. We can only find happiness in what our inner voice says. So, we better start having a positive inner voice or we are going to be an absolute mess. Rebecca's already there…

The next morning started the same as every day before it. Rebecca skipped breakfast, telling herself she would grab something from her drawer at work where she kept all her protein bars and snacks. She didn't have time for her own breakfast because she had to get the kids their breakfast and pack their lunches. Then it was rushing out the door trying to get the kids to school on time. It was always a rush trying to get ready for her own workday while getting the kids ready. Her husband's job started early, but ended early, which worked well for the family. She could get the kids ready for school and drop them off on the way to work, while her husband could pick them up from school and spend the afternoons with them on their homework, sports, music, and everything else. It worked efficiently.

After dropping the kids off at school she swung by the Starbucks to get her morning coffee and then it was off to work for another day. The long drive to work left her plenty of time to think about her life. But she hated to think about her life. So, she turned up her music and tried to lose the negative thoughts that were climbing into her head...

Who am I? What kind of life is this? Who am I going to let down today? Can I really keep doing this over and over? I have to be so many things for so many people. Manager. Employee. Wife. Mother. Sister. Daughter. Friend. Boss. Leader. Supporter. Listener. The list just keeps getting longer and longer. I'm tired. I'm worn out. I'm lost. Who am I really? How can I be all those things and yet I can't tell anyone who I really am. Will I ever get *me* back again?

She found her parking spot and walked in for another day of work. But when she got to the door of the building, she found Ed, one of the company's maintenance guys, putting a sign up on the door. "Good morning Ed, how's your day going so far?" Rebecca asked the older man. Ed laughed and shook his head, "Well it definitely could be better. What a mess. Didn't you get the email?" Rebecca shook her head.

"Oh man, it would've saved you a trip down here. We had to close the building down. One of the water pipes busted early this morning and started flooding the floor. It fried all the electrical stuff and a bunch of the computers. So, the bosses closed up shop and everybody is supposed to take the day off. They were supposed to send an email out." Rebecca looked at the man in amazement, "Are you serious Ed?" She tried to never check her email in the mornings because it was the few moments of each day that she got to spend with her kids. It was a boundary she was trying to set that at least for that part of the day she would put work aside.

The old man laughed and said, "Yeah, didn't you notice the work trucks and the guys here to fix everything?" Rebecca looked around and suddenly noticed a bunch of trucks and dozens of construction workers at the building. She was so lost in her own thoughts she had just walked in on auto mode, never noticing anything going on around her. "Lucky for you Rebecca, you get to go have a fun day. A day off, a chance to get out of the office for once. Go enjoy."

Once she had returned to her car, Rebecca just stared out the window at the building. She had no idea what she was going to do. She couldn't remember the last time she had a day off, especially while the kids were at school and her husband was at work. She sat there trying to think what she could do. Maybe this was a chance to catch up on a bunch of work she had been putting off. She had her laptop and she could easily work at the coffee shop nearby and knock out emails and reports and everything else. She pulled out her phone and called Farrah to see what she was up to.

Rebecca wasn't surprised at all to hear that Farrah was already hanging out at the beach. What a shocker, a twenty-something year old with no kids or family would be off having fun. Rebecca knew she would've done the same thing at that age. But her life was different now. She had people relying on her. When she told Farrah that she was planning to get some work done, Farrah jokingly scolded her, "Rebecca, you stop right there. It's a miracle day off. Do not work. Work will always be there tomorrow. Take the day and enjoy it. Find what you really love to do and go do it."

After she finished the call, Rebecca sat and thought about what Farrah had said. She was right that there would always be work ahead. There was no way to get caught up on everything. But Rebecca had fallen into a trap of always telling herself and others that once she had finished up the work she had to do, that then she would take some time off to do something fun. But she was never going to finish all her work. She was just telling people that as a defense mechanism to keep them off her back. Her phone beeped with a message. Farrah had shared an Instagram meme…

> For one day, put everything away…
> and take everything off your schedule…
> and do something you want to do…
> something you haven't done in awhile…
> something that will make YOU happy!

The message made Rebecca smile. She loved these kinds of memes and motivational pieces from social media. But could she really do what this message said? Could she really put everything to the side and do something she liked to do? Could she put herself ahead of everyone else in her life? She always worried that by putting her own interests and needs ahead of others that she would come across as selfish. She didn't want to be seen as selfish, because she wasn't selfish. But she thought it was what people would think of her. Then she thought about the situation she faced. No one except her colleagues knew that she had the day off. And they weren't going to apply any pressure to her, because most of them would be doing what Farrah was doing... having fun. Her family had no idea she had the day off. And even if they did, none of them were home anyways...

> What do I really want to do today? What would truly make me happy? What would help me get out of my rut, even just for a day? What have I been missing?

Then it came to her. The thing she missed most in her rut of busyness was working out. She missed being healthy. She missed her yoga sessions. She loved doing yoga. She loved how she felt when she was at Lea's Life Studio. She missed the rejuvenating feeling of being in a session. It made her body feel better. It made her head feel better. It made her feel relaxed. It always opened her mind and thoughts. She didn't feel trapped there. She didn't feel overwhelmed. It was as though there was a force field around her, not allowing anyone or anything else into her inner circle. Nothing could affect her there. It was her safe space. No technology. No family. No work. No problems. No reports. No files. No complaints. Just her and her thoughts and her body. That is where she needed to be today. That is what she needed.

It may sound very cliché to find your refuge for your life. We hear it all the time. Go to your happy place. Close your eyes and think about a place where you're truly happy. It sounds cliché because it truly works. Not just in our minds, but physically as well. We all need a place where we feel our best. We all need a place where we feel comfortable and safe and happy. We all need a refuge from the busyness of our lives. We need a refuge from the voices that surround us and tell us the negatives. We need a refuge where we can only hear our own inner voice. We need a refuge that gives us an escape from the world around us. We need a refuge that hides us from the negativity that exists all around us. It doesn't have to be a yoga session like it is for Rebecca. Your refuge can be anything you want it to be.

For some, it's a special place where they like to go. Maybe a particular spot in the woods where you connect with nature. Maybe it's laying out on the beach listening to the waves.

Maybe it's your favorite bench on the vista point looking out over the mountains. Maybe it's that spot under the tree in your yard where you can hear the birds. Wherever it is, it has to be your place, not someone else's. For some it's a hobby. Something that you love to do that turns your brain off for a while and lets you have fun. Maybe it's golfing. Or shopping. Or crocheting. Or cooking. Or reading a book. Or scrapbooking. Maybe it's gardening. Whatever it is, it has to be your hobby, not someone else's. For some it's a physical activity. Maybe a quiet walk through nature. Or going for a run with your music pumping. Maybe it's a fitness workout. Or it's taking a drive through the winding road on the coast. Maybe it's taking your dog for a walk in the park. Or working on a decorating project at your house. Whatever it is, it has to be your activity, not someone else's.

We have to figure out where or what our refuge is. It has to be a place where we can unplug from life. Where we can turn off our tech. Where we can get away from social media. Where we can get in tune with our inner thoughts, needs, and interests. A place where we feel safe, relaxed, comfortable, at ease, at peace. It has to be a place where we can tune out all of the outside world and recharge. It has to make us feel well. It has to shine a positive light on our life.

If we can't find this refuge and go there often, then we are doomed to being stuck in the rut. It's one thing to know where or what this place is, but we also have to actually go there regularly. We have to have the confidence to take time for ourselves. We have to allow ourselves to take a time out from life knowing that the world will not crumble around us. We have to allow ourselves time to be ourselves.

After returning home to drop off her work stuff and get changed into her workout gear, Rebecca made her way to the yoga studio. Through the years, she had been to plenty of yoga classes in gyms and fitness centers. Most of them were fine, but too often the yoga classes caused her to again think outside of herself. She would get caught up in how others were dressed or who else was in the class. But at Lea's Life Studio, the vibe was different. It was relaxing. No competition. It was perfect for her inner voice to be heard.

When she walked in and found her spot in the studio, Rebecca looked around. Her eyes immediately picked up on the sign in the corner of the room. It was where Lea always wrote a daily mantra that would lead her sessions for the day. It read "Turn down the negativity around you. Turn up the positivity inside of you." She smiled and thought...

If only I knew how to do that. If only I could control the volume button. I lost that inner voice in the busyness of life. I need to find it again soon. I don't

> like where my life is at this point. I want better. I need
> better. I deserve better.

As the session got started, Rebecca realized how badly she needed this in her life. She became very thankful for however that pipe got busted. She thought about how she would have been stuck in her office right then rather than reconnecting with her life on this yoga mat. She realized how badly she needed to find time for yoga.

The class moved into the Downward Dog Pose, which provided Rebecca the opportunity to focus in on her own thoughts. She was turning the world around her down and she was trying to turn up the volume on her own life, just like the sign had said. She couldn't remember the last time she had actually sat and reflected on life. She was always way too busy for that. She was too busy for anything for herself. It was work. It was family. It was friends. It was never her. She only had herself to blame she told herself. Zero balance. Zero control. It was like the world was a giant puppeteer controlling her strings as she danced on the little stage.

Everything was out of balance. Everyone was asking more and more and more of her and she felt like she had nothing left to give. She had lost herself in the pushes and pulls from all areas of her life. She was trying to give 100% of herself to every aspect of her life, but this was causing her to feel like she was giving nothing to anything. She was always working. She was working through her lunch hour. She was going all day without eating. If it wasn't for mochas from Starbucks, she wasn't sure she would actually take in any calories during a day. Yet her weight seemed to only be going up. She felt so unhealthy. She couldn't remember the last time she did anything just for herself. Not for her husband. Not for her kids. Not for her employees. Not for her bosses. Not for her friends. Not for her mom. Not for anybody except herself…

> As director of human resources, I send out constant emails and videos and reminders to employees to take care of their health and wellness. I give great tips and ideas that I find from experts on how to stretch, walk around, and sit correctly at desks. I share tips on how to take five-minute walks outside to destress. I send emails talking about how to live a balanced life between work and home and that nothing at work should be more important than their own life. And yet do I follow what I preach… no way no how. It's like that saying, *"Do as I say, not as I do."* What a fake leader I am. I can't even get that right.

She breathed in and back out and moved into the next phase of the pose. She realized she needed to change. She needed to find the balance again. Nothing at work is worth dying over. Nothing at work is worth losing a family over. Nothing at work is worth losing herself over. As she wrapped up the pose, she noticed the board again: "Turn down the negativity around you. Turn up the positivity inside of you." She knew she couldn't do it all in one day, but this day, this session, this reflection was fully capable of jumpstarting her balance.

One of the most difficult things to find in our lives is true balance. And no, we're not just talking about your yoga abilities! Balance always seems just out of reach. It's for the day when we finish this next project... the next set of laundry... the next vacation... the next workout... the next week. The problem is *next* never ever seems to get there though. We are always telling ourselves that we will get to balancing our life the next time. It's a way of giving ourselves an out. Things we don't want to do, or feel like we can't do, we put off to the next time. Think about all the things in your life that you say to yourself, "I'll do it the next time." The list is super long and includes things like... I'll start eating healthy next week... I'll leave work on time the next day I don't have a project to finish... I'll give my kid a consequence the next time they act out... I'll call my parents back the next time I have some free time... and so on, and so on, and so on infinitely!!!

When we are living in the trap of *the next time* we are not living in balance. A lack of balance can destroy our health, happiness, and wellness. It can affect our mental abilities, our physical abilities, and our emotional abilities. The more out of balance we get, the less likely we are to succeed on even the most minimal of tasks. When we are pushing too hard in one area of our life then we are pulling back from another. This is what Rebecca is struggling with. She's afraid of trying to get to a balanced position because she's afraid it means she's going to fail in other parts of her life. It's that moment in our yoga session where we are being challenged with a new balancing pose. Our brain tells us we aren't sure we can do it. We allow fear to creep in. We allow anxiety to take hold of us. It tenses our body. And as we begin to lift that leg to our balance point, we start hopping around trying not to fail. In reality, our anxiety and negative self-talk is what has actually caused us to fail.

We do this to ourselves all the time. We let ourselves off the hook. We let the fear of failure tell us that we can't make it. We can't find balance because our world will come crashing down. The worst part is we often then focus on the aspect of our lives that ultimately means the least to our happiness and health and wellness… our work. Too many of us give everything to work, to making money, to being successful. And while this push is needed, what's it pulling out of us?

This only gets more truncated in terms of our leadership abilities. As leaders we can't be stuck out of balance. It makes us edgy and short and emotional and tired and burned out.

Not exactly a list of great qualities for a leader, right? Leaders need balance so that they can feel good, think clearly, and make great decisions. We have to think deeply about how we can balance ourselves. Then we have to take our time and slowly move ourselves towards that balance point. Just like in yoga, no sudden movements because we will fall down. Instead, slow, methodical movements towards balance will leave us better leaders than we can ever imagine.

Eventually Rebecca and the rest of the class moved to the Wide-Legged Forward Bend, which was a new pose for her. As she held the pose with her hands outstretched behind her back while she looked backwards through her own legs, she again became consumed with her inner thoughts. She was truly turning up the voice inside her... a voice she hadn't heard from in a long time. She remembered how that voice used to be so positive. It used to pump her up before big meetings and presentations. It used to tell her she was amazing and smart and talented and wonderful. It used to tell her she looked good. It used to tell her she was a good wife, a good mother, a good daughter, a good sister. But over the course of the years, the voice had quieted down. It had been replaced by the voices she thought she heard around her, in the social media she looked at, in the conversations she had with people in her life.

She is down on herself constantly. She beats herself up emotionally. She's all about the negative voice in her head telling her how she is letting everyone down. How she is nothing. She isn't good enough. When she sees the posts on Facebook from her mom friends about how they were at their kids' school for a performance... she calls herself a terrible mom for not being there and instead being at work. The voice inside her has been telling her she's a bad mom... a bad wife... a bad employee... a bad leader... a bad daughter... a bad sister. Just simply... bad at everything...

> How did this happen to me? I used to be so strong. So amazing. So talented. So confident. So proud of myself. And yet it's all gone. How do I get it back? How can I be who I used to be?

As she continued to move through the pose, she realized how quickly she had picked up the difficult move. She was breezing through this yoga session even though it had probably been months since she had last been to Lea's. It was like riding a bicycle, it just came back so easy. It was there the whole time, just hiding behind all the doubt and self-deprecation. Hiding behind all the negative self-talk...

> If I can catch up so quickly on my yoga after it's been so long, why can't I do it for my confidence? It shouldn't be any different. Yoga isn't easy. This pose isn't easy. And yet I know that I can do it. And I am doing it. I am really good at this. I am really good at a

> lot of things. No matter what I think people say about me, I know I'm a good mother. I'm a good leader. I'm a good wife. I'm a good person.

Suddenly a flood of memories came streaming in. It was like she had broken down a dam that was holding back this massive lake of emotions and confidence. The negative self-talk had continued to build this dam. The taller it had gotten the more difficult it was to see all that was great about her life on the other side. But it was time to knock down the dam. It was time to bust a hole right through it. And did she ever bust a hole. She suddenly thought about all the great things that she had done in her life.

Her job is amazing because she helps people to find their voice and their confidence and to not doubt themselves or how they feel. She has two beautiful, smart, and talented kids who are excelling in school and sports and music. They are funny and energetic and sweet. While she and her husband fight more than they used to, they have a good marriage. They trust each other and love each other. They make each other happy. She thinks about all the people who turn to her for help in their lives. She is always there for them. It may take a lot out of her, but would she want it any other way?

As Rebecca came out of her pose, she realized that everything is different when you look at it differently. A new lens that is positive can change how you see the world. Instead of telling herself how awful everything is, she can find the positives. As she stood waiting for the next pose, she could feel the confidence pouring through her body. She is who she is. And she is damn good at it. She must believe in herself. She must build on this confidence. She must see life differently. She must see herself differently.

When we are younger it's easy to find confidence in some way in our life, but as we grow older it becomes harder and harder to find. Why is this? Because there are so many aspects of our life that can suck out our confidence. The world seems to throw things at us constantly that are like magnets for our confidence. It seems so easy to lose and the more times we lose our confidence, the harder it is to find it again. Losing our confidence becomes more and more difficult to handle each time. The more that we lose it we become less able to believe that we ever actually had it to begin with. We become disconnected and frustrated.

Confidence can be such a tricky thing to deal with in our lives. As we lose our confidence, what takes over... that's right... self-doubt. We begin the negative talk about ourselves. We tell ourselves we aren't worth it. We were never good at it. We basically tell ourselves that we suck. It's because we have heard from so many people and situations in our lives that we are failing. This is what Rebecca is dealing with. She's getting negative feedback. She's telling herself she is terrible at everything. She's telling herself she can't succeed no matter what she tries. And this self-doubt acts as a blindfold for trying to find her confidence.

For us as leaders, a lack of confidence and an over-bearing level of self-doubt will destroy our ability to lead. Nobody wants to follow a wishy-washy leader, who is full of doubt and doesn't believe in their own abilities. How can you trust a leader like that? How can you believe in someone that doesn't even believe in themselves? Leaders are confident people who believe in their abilities, which attracts followers who find it easy to believe and trust in a confident leader.

What Rebecca is dealing with is something we all deal with in our lives. We live our lives outside of ourselves. We live our lives based on everyone around us. We live by what others think of us. We live by what others say about us. Most of the time, it isn't even what they say or do, but rather what we assume they say or think about us. We make up stories that fit our negative narrative. These stories are built off things we have heard from somebody in our life, and so we begin to think everyone thinks that about us. Think about if one of your kids or employees says you aren't doing a good job. Suddenly you become hyper aware of this idea. You begin to think that everyone must think this about you. You don't know for sure, so you fill in the void with the story that they all think that about you. It changes how you act. It changes how you lead. It changes who you are.

But what if we instead told ourselves that person is an outlier, or they are just pissed and trying to attack us personally. They know what will hurt us and they are preying on us. Wouldn't that help us to know they are not the norm, that what they think of us isn't what everyone thinks about us. Wouldn't we be happier and more confident? It all comes down to our levels of the **Authentic Element of Leadership**. The biggest component of this element is our ability to be self-aware, original, and confident. When you are living in balance with the Authentic Element of Leadership you know exactly who you are and what makes you tick. You're balanced. You're reflective. You're confident. You believe in yourself.

This Element is aligned to the sixth chakra of yoga, known as the seeing or brow chakra, which concentrates on intuition, awareness, clarity, and inner wisdom. In this Element, it's not about leading the same way as everybody else. It's not about trying to fit in. It's not about trying to be what you think everyone expects from you. It's not about living outside of yourself. It's not about hearing what the world is telling you. It's about knowing who you are, the skills you have, the talents you can use, and then going and doing it. It isn't about making sure everyone likes your style or methods. It's about being you through meditation and self-reflection. It comes from finding balance in your life. It comes from replacing negative self-talk with positive self-talk. It comes from turning down the negativity around you and turning up the positivity inside of you.

Just like Rebecca is doing in this story, in order to grow your Authentic Element of Leadership, you have to figure out who you are, what you want out of life, what makes you happy, what makes you healthy. For every person it may be different. You must figure out who you are by reflecting, then identifying what makes you tick, and then believing in yourself that you can do that. Notice at no point is the suggestion to go to everybody around you to ask them for their opinion! This Element of Leadership is about you and only you. It's about having confidence in who you are, no matter what others say about you. It's about not just talking the talk but walking the walk.

The session had ended, and Rebecca couldn't have been feeling better about herself. She knew that she couldn't change her entire life in a single yoga session, but the fact that she had chosen to go to that session spoke volumes for what she truly needed and wanted in her life. She wanted to feel good and healthy and happy and confident. She had lost herself somewhere, but today she saw herself for the first time in a long time. But there was no way she was going to lose it again. There was no way she could go back to the way she had been living. It wasn't good for her.

As she walked towards the door with a renewed energy for finding herself and bringing balance to her life, she felt a tap on her shoulder. She turned around to see Lea walking by her side. Rebecca smiled and reached out to hug her. Lea whispered into her ear, "It is so good to see you again Rebecca. We missed you." Rebecca felt tears welling up in her eyes. She was embarrassed that it had been so long since she had last been to a class. Lea pulled back from the hug, but still held Rebecca's arms in hers. "Do not worry about what I think of you. Do not worry about what anyone here thinks of you. No judgment. No embarrassment. No shame. No doubt. Everyone has their own path in life. Don't ever let someone else's path tell you what your path should be. You are the only you that you can be. So be proud of you. Believe in you. Live the life you want to live."

Rebecca wiped the tears at her eyes and said, "Turn down the negativity and turn up the positivity, right?" Lea giggled and nodded her head as she replied, "Wow, it's like that message was written just for you, right. It's not magic, it's all about how we can receive the messages we want to receive from the world. What we want to find in our lives, we will find, just like that message." Rebecca thanked her and told her how Lea would be seeing a lot more of her in class.

When Rebecca got out to her car, she thought about how this was the time where she would always immediately pull out her phone and see if she had any voicemails, emails, or messages from work. But she caught herself as she started to get her phone out. She wasn't going to check work stuff, but rather she was going to call her husband. She told him about her day off and that she was now heading to the kids' school to volunteer in their classroom. When he asked her why, she told him the truth, "Because it's what I want to do with my afternoon." It was who she was. She wasn't going to let work get in the way of that. She would have plenty of work the next day, but for at least this day, she was a mom.

After signing in at the elementary school and putting on her visitor pass, she headed off to her daughters' classes. The reaction was the same from both of her little girls when she went into each of their rooms. They came running over and jumped into her arms with a huge hug. One of her daughters told her just what she needed to hear, "Of all the moms in the world, I would pick you as my mom every time." The words made her smile and cry all in the same motion, but she loved it. She knew it wasn't just because she had shown up that day, it was because she was a good person. And a good woman. She was exactly who she was meant to be. After the school day ended, she drove the girls back home. Later that evening, she found herself sitting out on the patio playing a board game with her kids. Her husband was barbecuing, and the dogs were running around being goofy. She was taking time to enjoy her life.

She thought about posting some pictures of her day on her social media accounts but stopped herself. She thought who cares what the world sees about her… as long as she was happy… that was all that mattered. And she knew she was happy. She never wanted this end… to never go back to work. But she knew she could choose to have this life. Because balance is up to her. Confidence is up to her. Happiness is up to her. She doesn't have to post this moment on Facebook or check in with the world around her to know if she's winning in life. She already knows because the voice inside her is talking again and she is actually listening to the words…

Turn down the negativity around me.
Turn up the positivity inside of me.

The Impact Element

It was early in the morning, just the way Lea liked to start her day. The sun was just coming up and the earliest light in the sky was dazzling off a pack of clouds that hung low over the cityscape. The morning air was cool and refreshing. Lea walked up to her studio and felt her breath connecting with the air around her. It was peaceful and serene. It was beautiful and awe-inspiring. She went in through the door and locked it behind her. The morning sunlight was just coming in through the windows of the studio and it hung like a dim spotlight illuminating the completely calm and empty space within the studio. She found a spot right near the windows and rolled out her mat.

Lea loved leading yoga sessions. She loved working with people all day long. It was an amazing experience to see so many different people come in and out of the doors all day long. They were all different and unique. They were special to her because they gave her purpose for her life. But as much as she longed for a filled room every session, her early morning solitude was her favorite time of the day. It was because it was her opportunity to work on herself, without the hustle and bustle of running a business, leading sessions, and talking with people. It was just her and her studio, her and her mat, her and her yoga, her and her breath. Before anyone showed up for a class, she would take herself through her own routine, working on various aspects of her own chakras, trying to be in tune with what she needed at that time. She started every day that way. It always energized her for the day ahead and prepared her to open the studio to the masses who were looking for more from their own life.

Lea could see the sun shining ever so slightly through the clouds as though they were rays from the heavens. One particular beam of light was shining right in the window and onto the crown of her head. She took it as a sign to focus on her crown chakra and to reflect and meditate on her life. She smiled because it made her happy when she could feel the connection with the universe. Lea set out into her routine, eventually finding herself on her knees, moving into Rabbit Pose. She arched her back as she moved her head down onto the mat looking at her knees. Her hands were extended behind her, holding onto the soles of her feet. Holding onto her feet make her think about how taking one step at a time had helped in the earliest parts of her own journey.

She had been a teenager when Lea was forced to leave her home and move to another country on the other side of the world. It was the Vietnam War that had changed her life forever. It was how she had ended up in America, a refugee teenager whose family was fleeing the violence that had destroyed the world of so many families. She had been told that she and her family had been the lucky ones, because many families did not find their escape. Lives were lost. Families were destroyed. A country was torn apart. And yet all she ever heard from everyone was how lucky she was to get a fresh start in America. But her new life had not been easy. Everything was new. Everything brought change. A new language to learn. New customs and traditions to learn. New friends to make. New streets to walk. And yet the entire time, her family tried to hold onto the traditions and customs that made them who they were.

Her teenage years had been extremely difficult. She dealt with prejudice at every turn. She was made fun of at times. She felt alone on so many days. Change was difficult. This change seemed impossible at times. There were so many days where she dreamed of the life she had before as a small child. One of the only things she found solace in was being with her grandmother who had come with her family to this new world. Her grandmother was a yogini, having taught yoga for years in their home country. Lea spent many days in America with her grandmother as her parents worked countless jobs to make ends meet. She found herself waiting all day in school to go to her grandma's house where she felt safe and comfortable. And every afternoon she would do yoga with her grandma. She loved those moments. She loved the way she felt when she did her yoga. She loved how it gave her an opportunity to reflect and think about her life.

Lea's love for yoga became a deep passion and she began seeking opportunities to learn more about yoga. In her senior year of high school, she took a job in a local yoga studio. It was pretty basic work like maintaining the facility, cleaning mats, sweeping floors, and putting equipment away, but she loved the job because she got to participate in classes for free. One of the aspects of yoga that she loved so much was the idea of focusing in on one breath or one step or one move. It was what she had been doing her entire life since coming to America. This concept made complete sense.

She continued to take one step after another as she became a certified yoga instructor. Soon she was teaching classes all over town. She taught at senior centers and rec centers, adult schools, and in studios. She was piecing one class after another together, building a momentum of growth for her career. She never went to college. Her family couldn't afford it and her move to America caused her to struggle in school. But she loved yoga and she wanted to see where that path would take her. The momentum was gaining in her life.

The word momentum really struck Lea as she continued to reflect in her Rabbit Pose. It reminded her of one of her students named Salma, an absolutely scared, anxious, and completely overwhelmed young woman who had come into her studio. She could remember how Salma had struggled to take those small steps on the path of her life, but through her yoga practice had learned to focus on the smallest details, rather than the massivity of the world around her.

Lea came up out of her Rabbit Pose and paused. She smiled as she remembered the day Salma had swung by the studio with a picture of her non-profit team working with a United Nations relief team in the Middle East. The partnership between Salma's non-profit and the UN started because Salma's marketing team created a social media ad campaign that went viral and the UN called wanting to work together to make a difference. And what a difference they were making all because Salma had begun living...

**One breath at a time. One move at a time.
One step at a time.**

Lea moved into her next pose, one that she really enjoyed because it was challenging... the Thunderbolt Pose. She leaned backwards and extended her stomach forward towards the sky. She wrapped herself backwards and placed the crown of her head on the ground between her outstretched feet. She reached out and held onto her knees. She could feel the stretching pull move through her body, especially in her hips and upper legs. She paused and breathed in and out. She was one with her thoughts again.

It reminded her of her earliest days leading yoga sessions. At that time, she was just in survival mode, trying to build a career and a client list. She was teaching classes everywhere while focused on her role and routines. But she wasn't truly connecting with the people in her classes. Lea had built great sequences filled with good poses that people needed, but she always felt separated from the people in her classes. They would come in and participate, but then leave right away. There was no community or relationships being built. She was trying, but it just wasn't working the way Lea wanted it to. She was so nervous about her basic survival as a yoga teacher. She felt she had to make people happy enough that they'd come back to her class. If not, she would've been out of a job. It wasn't about challenging people to see the world or themselves differently. Her classes were all about a series of poses built together, but the people lacked feeling and connectivity. She was struggling to move away from a focus on poses and into what yoga could really offer holistically.

Then one day, her grandma shuffled into the rec center where Lea was teaching her class. Her grandma's health was failing at that time and so she found a seat on a chair at the back of the room. Lea's grandma watched the class in silence, just taking it all in. After the session had ended, Lea skipped over and gave her a huge hug. Her grandma smiled and asked her, "What do you feel when you hug me?" Lea looked at her inquisitively not really understanding what her grandma was getting at. But Lea responded, "I feel love. I feel connected to you. I feel all that we have been through together. I feel happiness. I feel joy."

Lea's grandma smiled as she saw the tears rolling down her granddaughter's face. "Oh, you sweet thing. You are precious. But let me ask you, do you think your students feel that way about their yoga?" Lea shook her head because she knew they didn't, and it frustrated her. "Lea, that feeling you have when you hug me is what yoga is all about. It isn't just about a move or a pose… it's about love. It's about feeling something about yourself and about others around you. And it all begins with you as the teacher. You have to find that feeling. And you have to share that feeling with your class. You need them to feel the hug from yoga. You need them to feel the love from yoga. You need to be the leader."

It was a moment that had changed Lea's life forever. Her grandma died only a few weeks later, and it was a conversation that Lea never ever forgot. Because it changed who Lea was, not only as a yoga teacher, but as a person. She began to reflect more and connect more with her own love for yoga. She began to think less about the poses and more about the feelings that yoga provided. And she took this renewed love and filled her classes with it. She focused on connecting with the people who came into her classes. She focused on mantras that she began writing on a little white board with a dry erase marker. She wanted her classes to be about emotion and growth and love and connectivity.

And as she changed, so to do the students in her classes. She was finally leading others not just teaching them. Lea could feel the love in the room. She could feel the connections with her students. She became in tune with their lives outside of the class and began to read their emotions and connect with them at a deeper level. And every single time she felt that love from someone in her class she would think of her grandma… she would think of the woman that enabled her to instill so much love into the world around her.

As Lea came back out of her Thunderbolt Pose, she could feel the tears that had been flowing from her eyes. She knelt there just letting the tears fall, not clearing them away or trying to make them stop. This was what yoga was about. This was the feeling she loved. And as she sat in her tears, she couldn't help but think of the young man who came to her looking for the exact same feeling in his life. That sweet young man named Alden had shut out the world around him for so long that he didn't think he could ever let anyone in. Even Lea had been worried about him, but she treated him with love and patience. She wanted to connect with him because she knew connectivity was the one thing that could break down the walls he had built around himself.

Lea's tears came down even harder as she remembered the day only a few months back when Alden and his love Tallulah had visited her before one of her classes. They both had been regulars in her class for so long, and their love story had actually begun right in her studio, but they hadn't been around for a few months. So, when they walked in that door, she was so surprised to see them. And the best part of it all was that they came in with their beautiful baby girl. Alden had hugged Lea as he introduced the old yogi to his daughter... Lea Lochlan. The old yogi had broken down crying at their use of her name for their daughter, especially when Alden shared with her that if it wasn't for the old yogi, then their love story would have never started. And it was all because Alden had made the effort to...

**Break down my walls and
build bridges to others around me.**

Lea shifted her body around. She put her hands down and then lifted her body up until her knees were resting on her elbows. She pushed her legs up into the air and lifted her body up off the mat... a strong Handstand Pose. She began to contort her legs around into various poses, as she focused in on her balance. It was a pose based on balancing and movement and it made her think about the actions she took to change her life forever through her yoga practice. After teaching for years in various centers and locations, Lea had built up a strong number of clients and participants who sought out her classes. But the people were finding it difficult to locate her classes as she was always on the move, trying to find locations to work from. Lea had decided it was time to focus on the next steps of her career.

At the time, Lea had grown to know many different people in the community. She was asking questions of the owners of gyms, centers, and studios so she could learn as much as she could about the business side of yoga. She had always dreamed of owning her own studio, but she knew it was a huge step. No longer would she just be able to teach, letting the owners of the studios and centers she worked at deal with the business side. If she was going to open her own studio, she was going to have to be ready for all the business aspects, which were things Lea knew very little about. As she researched how to start a business, she was realizing there were a million things she was going to have to do. It felt overwhelming and intimidating. How could just one woman take all of that on? So, she hesitated for a while as she continued to do what she loved to do, which was to teach yoga. But the urge to make it on her own was yearning daily.

She dealt with a lot of doubt during that time. There was a ton of self-questioning talk. She wasn't entirely sure she could handle all of it. Was she strong enough? Was she smart enough? Was she talented enough? The questions hit her at every turn. And yet, she knew inside that if she could start her own studio, then she could do things the way she wanted to. She could teach courses the way she wanted to. She could build the environment the way she wanted it to be. She could have a set place where her clients could come regularly. The voice inside of her kept telling her she did have what it took to do something amazing. And yet she remained frozen until a day when a little old lady named Esther came to talk to her.

Esther had been coming to Lea's senior center yoga classes for years. She loved yoga and was always telling Lea that it was a great way to keep herself from getting old. Esther was a woman in her 90s, yet her spirit was young and vibrant, and she loved yoga. After one of the classes, she came up to Lea and wanted to talk to her. She insisted that Lea needed her own place to teach in, because Lea's personality and quirky style and sessions just didn't fit into the stale senior center environment. Lea shared with Esther how she had always wanted to start her own studio, but she was stuck trying to take the first step, because there were a million other steps to take after that one. Little old Esther leaned into Lea and said, "You are correct that the first step is always the most difficult, but sometimes all somebody needs is a gentle little push to get started. How about I give you that push so you can make your dreams come true and you can impact many people?" Lea wasn't quite sure what the little lady meant. But she soon figured it out as Esther handed Lea a folder with official documents inside.

The documents were the title and deed paperwork for a building. Esther smiled at Lea and said, "My husband and I owned this building for years. It was where our family business had been located. We grew up as a family in that building. We built our business. We raised our kids. We built a life together. But as you know he died several years ago after 64 years of marriage. Even though our business closed years ago, we held onto the building. I kept telling myself I needed to sell it, especially with the market doing so well now. But there was something inside of me that kept holding onto it. I knew it needed something special. And now I want to give it to you to start your own studio." Lea didn't know quite what to say. She was shocked, "Oh, I couldn't Esther, you should sell it and make money. Plus, I am not even sure I could handle starting a business…"

The little old lady reached out and held onto Lea's arm. "No, I do not need the money and neither do my kids or grandkids. They have always been well taken care of and they will again when I pass on. But I have thought about it a lot and I want the building to be used for great things. And there are few people in my life who have had as great an impact as you have. You see, after my husband died, I stayed by myself in my house and didn't want to leave. We had been together since we were teens and had been through so many things in life. I was alone and scared and sad. I wasn't sure I wanted to live without him. But that all changed when my friend Opal asked if I could give her a ride to the senior center for a quilting class because her car had broken down. I came that day with her and I was looking around the center as I waited for her to finish her class. Nothing really caught my interest as I checked things out until I walked by this room right here. You were inside with a class of old people like me. And they were actually doing yoga. They seemed happy. I thought to myself I want to feel that way. I've been coming every week since and I can't tell you how much you've done for me and my life. I want that to continue for others, long after I have left this world. So please take the studio and start taking the steps to making your business happen, because I just pushed you past the first really hard step."

Lea was speechless. She wrapped the old lady in her arms and held her in a hug as tears began streaming from the faces of both women. Esther had been right. It was the push at the right time in Lea's life. Lea accepted the gift of the building and took off running into her business after that. She never stopped working those first couple of years, wearing every hat a small business owner must wear. But she was building a special business, one that was going to help thousands of Esther's for years to come.

Lea brought her legs back down to the ground and got out of her Handstand Pose. She began thinking about how her own journey of action was similar to the action-packed, fast-paced lightning bolt she knew as Taylor. That young woman was so gifted and yet she too was frozen in her business. She was overwhelmed with so many hats to wear that she had just gotten stuck in what to do next. But she eventually figured it out and wow, how she got it going. Lea had even seen Taylor on TV as a guest on a late-night talk show. Yeah, the same woman stuck in neutral, was now driving in the fast lane. People were coming from all over the world to attend her workshops. Taylor was a star and an inspiration to women all over the world. And it was all because Taylor had made the effort in her life to tell herself...

**I am strong. I am powerful.
I am confident. I believe in myself.**

Lea moved into her Standing Forward Bend Pose. Her favorite version of this pose was to wrap her arms around her legs as she bent forward with her head pressed in against the front of her legs. She loved this version because she felt like it was a way to show herself that she was loved. It brought back the feelings of hugging her grandma. It made her feel love and compassion. It simply made her heart feel warmth and care. And this was important to her because that is what her entire life was centered on through her yoga practice. She wanted the people who came to her classes to not just get the health benefits in terms of their fitness and flexibility, but that they would be emotionally healthy and find their own love for themselves.

The compassionate gift that Esther had given Lea was not ever forgotten. It was an inspiring and motivating example of what Lea wanted her business to be all about. As her studio grew, Lea never lost sight of the entire point of her studio – to focus on her clients and their love for the world around them. She wanted them to find that which empowered them to be like Esther and to pay forward the feelings that they had onto other people. It wasn't about Lea and what she needed, instead Lea wanted the best for every person who came through her door. She wanted them to feel different when they were in the studio. She wanted them to carry that difference out into the world with them. Lea knew that every great change in the world and society began with the simplest of actions and she hoped that her work could inspire others to move towards that change.

With Esther always in mind, Lea set out a plan to offer free classes for groups that needed yoga but couldn't afford to attend a class. Not every class was free, it was a business, and Lea needed to survive herself, but she knew that she could give away a portion of her time for others who needed help. She began by offering free daily sessions in the late mornings that were only for seniors. She knew that so many of them were on fixed retirement incomes and couldn't afford to take part in yoga. But this wasn't even enough for her. She went to local retirement communities and senior living facilities and worked out deals to bus people over to her studio a couple of days a week to attend senior yoga. Every time she would run one of these classes it would fill her heart with joy and love at the sight of these old people smiling and happy.

Her compassionate work didn't stop there. She began to put on weekend yoga sessions for low-income families. She booked time in her studio on the weekends even though weekends were a great money maker in many studios for all the career working people who couldn't make it to classes during the week. But she passed up on the money to instead give back to people that were just like her family. Working tirelessly to put food on the table and to keep their children clean and clothed. As a child, her own family didn't have the money for her mom or dad to go pay for a yoga session. But why shouldn't they have access to the benefits of yoga? Lea's financial advisor at the time didn't think it made good business sense. So, she switched to a new financial advisor who understood the compassionate side of her business and she kept offering the classes to the families in need.

The compassionate side had to be there. She didn't just want to be another money-focused health studio that only cared about the bottom line. She knew there was more to life than just money. Sure, she had to make money to put food on her own table and to keep the lights on in her studio, but she didn't need a ton more than that. And so, she gave back to those who needed a little boost. There was little in life more satisfying then seeing the faces of the people who came to those sessions. To see the calmness on their faces as they exited the building was so rewarding. It was what life was about in her opinion. She had been in their shoes. She had lived that life. She had been that refugee looking for a new opportunity. Yoga had saved her life from falling apart, so why not let it save others from their paths falling apart.

She breathed in deeply and exhaled. She let go of her hug around her legs and slowly stood back up. She lifted her head up and stood looking up at the ceiling as she slowly breathed in and out. She could feel her heart beating. She could feel the love coursing through her body. It was bliss. One of her all-time favorite students popped into her thoughts. She could remember Miguel sitting in his fancy car, not sure if he really wanted to come in. She had opened her arms and heart to him that day in the parking lot. She wasn't really sure it was going to work because he seemed very shook up. But he walked in that door, and Lea liked to think it was because she had shown him care and love and compassion. But even Lea couldn't have imagined the transformation he was going to go through. Miguel had become a compassionate and caring human being, while still rocking the business world. But his output was so much more powerful now because he was all about those who hadn't yet caught a break in life.

It was never more apparent than the day when he arrived in the studio for his regular yoga session but came to Lea with a request. He asked her if she'd be willing to come to his new community center in his old neighborhood and put on free yoga classes for the people of his neighborhood. Of course, Miguel shared with Lea, the classes would be free for the people, but he would definitely pay Lea anything it took to get her to come and teach. Lea remembered telling him that he didn't need to pay her a penny, as she was happy to help him with his outreach programs. And while Lea wouldn't accept any money for the efforts, Miguel being the man he was, of course wanted to pay it forward for Lea's volunteer work. He talked her into letting his construction team come in and help with a renovation and rejuvenation of the tiny and dilapidated Lea's Life Studio. The one thing he told his team to not touch at all was the sign on the front of the studio. The sign needed to stay as it was, because he could remember seeing it as he sat in front of the building not knowing his life was about to change forever. And it was all because Miguel had learned how to...

Make my life count.
Breathe out love, kindness, and compassion.

Lea crouched back down to her mat slowly and rhythmically. She knelt again on her knees with her feet extended behind her. She put her hands up over her head and slowly began to arch backwards, extending her spine until she had laid her back down on the mat. As she sat completely opened up with her arms out past her head, she breathed in deeply. Then she exhaled and felt her chest and throat feeling her every breath. She loved the Saddle Pose because she felt so ready to have her voice heard in those moments. She couldn't help but remember back to when she first realized her voice needed to be heard by so many people.

At a certain point after opening her studio, Lea really did find her voice. She found the part of her that separated her from so many other yogis and yoga studios. She loved to talk with her students and learn more about them. She loved to see them and build relationships with them by getting to know them at a deeper level. Every chance she got before and after class to talk with students filled her with joy. Every opportunity she could get inside of class to walk by a student and whisper to them about their practice or thoughts filled her with a sense of being. She loved to use her voice to help people, but she never saw her voice as a method to tell others what to do. Instead she used it to ask them questions, which made them think and develop their own ideas. She had always disliked people who would tell her what to do and what to think, or even worse who told her why her actions or words were wrong. She always thought of those people as being closed off and struggling to see the world around them from a fresh lens. Lea was all about new perspectives and new ways to see the world around her.

So, she asked her students questions and then listened to their answers. She tried to pick up what they really meant by the way in which they responded and the words that they used. She was less about telling people how to do things differently and more about helping them to figure it out on their own. And it was all about the questions she asked and the mantras that she shared. She loved mantras because while they did have a message within them, so many of them were really open to how the individual interprets them. To say *make my life count* was a strong message, but it could mean a hundred different things to a hundred different people. For Lea, her talks with people were about helping them to shed their blinders and to open their eyes and ears and minds and hearts to new possibilities. And it seemed to work for so many people. After a class would end, she would have a line of people who wanted to talk with her.

She had learned these skills from her own father. He was the strong silent type. Lea could always tell that he was deeply thinking about his life and the world around him. And when Lea would go to him for advice, he would always respond with questions. It was question after question, interrupted only by the sayings and quotes that he had found in the many books that he loved to read. He always said the quotes and sayings were there to bring meaning to life. They allow us to interpret them in our own authentic way. We can see them in a way that matches who we are at our core. As a kid, this approach really frustrated Lea. There were so many times where she just wanted an answer to her question or dilemma. But her dad believed in taking the time to figure out the answer in your own way. While being frustrated as a child with the approach, Lea had grown to love it and eventually to use it all day every day in her practice.

Lea rarely, if ever, gave actual hard advice to anyone. She tried to always be like her dad and speak in questions and quotes and mantras. Eventually people had come to expect this from Lea, and in fact, they sought it out. The key for her was that she didn't want people to rely only on the thoughts and ideas and words of other people. Because when they do that, how are they supposed to build and develop their own authentic selves? How can a person think and act on their own if they are constantly reliant on other people to do it for them? It was why she vowed to never tell people what to do, but rather open a door into their own hearts and minds to find the answer for themselves. It was a way for her to use her voice in a charismatic and inspiring and motivating manner that could impact others. The key was that by finding the answers for themselves, through deliberate questioning and prodding from Lea, they became confident in their own abilities and strengths. And with that confidence would come their own voice which they could use to inspire and motivate other people in their lives.

As she arched her body back up and out of her Saddle Pose, she returned again to her knees. She focused in on her breath as she tucked her chin down. She could feel it pressed against her throat. She felt in tune with her voice at that moment. Thinking about her own journey to find her voice and use it correctly, Lea thought back to the impact that one teacher's voice had on so many different people who needed help. And to think Shantel was one of the quietest and most unassuming people she had ever met. Shantel had always kept to herself. But eventually Shantel emerged from her shell with an incredible voice she used to speak out for those who had no voice. Shantel's voice became a multiplier as she began to teach others how to speak out in their own schools, communities, and neighborhoods.

Lea thought back to the envelope that arrived in the mail from Shantel. Inside of it was an invitation and a ticket to attend one of Shantel's motivational workshops. Lea could remember the smile she had at seeing the invite from a woman who had been *just* a teacher and was now a motivational speaker focused on helping educators to be a voice on their campus for change, particularly change that helped the students who needed help the most. Lea had sat in the audience that day and was so proud of the once quiet elementary school teacher who was now impacting kids everywhere. And it was because Shantel had figured out...

My voice is mighty when I speak
for those who are silenced.

Lea adjusted her weight from her knees up onto her toes. She found her balance and held herself there for a couple of breaths before she rotated her feet until her heels were touching each other which meant her knees were turned and facing out away from her body to either side. She then moved her hands from the prayer position until they were extended above her head with her palms pressed against each other and her elbows bent out to the side. Ahhhh... the Balancing Butterfly Pose. Lea always felt like it opened a window into her own soul and her own authentic being.

Her authentic self had changed and yet not changed over the years of her life. She had changed many times in terms of who she was and what she focused on. And yet, she hadn't changed who she was at the core. It was almost as though the word change was difficult to use in this case. It was more like she had adapted and evolved her inner self over time yet kept a foundational sense of self that had been with her since childhood. She was who she was, but it didn't mean she couldn't learn and grow as she went along. So much of life was about balancing different sides of ourselves and being able to move back and forth. Never too far one way and yet never too far back the other way.

For all the balance that she talked about with her students, there were times in her own career where she had struggled to find her balance. At one point she had struggled with that mid-career feeling of "Is this what I was supposed to be when I grew up?" She battled it for a while, searching for who she really was. What impact she actually had? If she should try something else? She knew that a lot of yogis were doing videos and online courses. She was worried that she would be left behind if she didn't. She considered it and thought she should try to learn the new way so that she wouldn't go out of business. She knew that everybody was doing everything on social media, but she was older and didn't really want to go through another big change. She eventually figured out that social media and videos were not her calling. She was meant to do exactly what she was doing in her small studio. It didn't matter if she was the richest or best yogi out there. She was good with who she was.

The struggle with balance and who she was also had hit her recently. Lea was now an older woman herself. Her closest friends had moved on into their retirement years and were vacationing and doing things in life that they couldn't do while they were working. And they were enjoying themselves. Lea had strongly considered retirement. She had thought about stopping her teaching. She had thought about just moving into a management role with the studio and letting others take over the classes and day-to-day management of the business. Over the years she had brought in others to work in the studio, teaching classes or working the front desk or handling the accounting. It had always helped her to keep her focus on the parts of the business she lived for... the yoga and the people.

But to completely walk away from it all just didn't fit who Lea was. It didn't matter how old she got or how much more difficult the moves might get for her to actually do. She absolutely loved what she did. Her own authentic self was so entwined with the yoga that to cut out the yoga and the business would be like cutting half of one's body off. There was just no way that she could walk away and go travel the world in a RV. There was nothing wrong with that at all, as many of her friends were doing just that, but that life just wasn't Lea. And if there was one thing people would say about Lea, it was that she was authentic. She knew who she was, and she lived who she was. And deep inside, she knew that she was one with the yoga and that she couldn't ever really walk away. It was who she was, and she was proud of it, but most of all, it made her happy.

Thinking about her authentic journey made Lea think of one of the most authentic women she had ever come across. Rebecca hadn't always been authentic as she was trapped by the world around her and the negative self-talk that she held herself down with. But Rebecca had changed it all. She had found herself and what made her truly happy and content in life. It had taken many years for her to figure it out, but when she did, it changed everything for her. She had cut back her hours and had even moved to a part time schedule working half days so she could be with her family more often. Lea loved seeing how Rebecca was happy every day, and she got to see it a lot because Rebecca had actually become a yoga instructor and was leading classes in Lea's studio. And it was all because Rebecca had learned how to…

Turn down the negativity around me.
Turn up the positivity inside of me.

What Lea is going through in this session is all about the **Impact Element of Leadership**. This Element is all about how we as leaders can change the world around us. We know it sounds like a tall order to change the world when we are only one tiny little person in the ginormous universe. How could you do anything as one person to impact so much? You may be doubting your own abilities to change the world, but what about Lea? Would you say she is changing the world? Can anyone really do that? They can. They have. Lea can. Lea has. *And so can you.*

We often fall into the trap of thinking that in order to make a difference we have to do something major or huge. We have to start a foundation. We have to start an initiative. We have to do something massive that fixes some huge problem in society. Homelessness. Hunger. Violence. Abuse. Racism. The list of huge items is massive. All of these big issues need leaders who can bring great change and make a difference. But making a difference doesn't have to only be at a massive level. It can be at a minimal or even an individual level. And even at that small level it can change the world.

Think about Lea's situation. She isn't a president or a world leader of any kind. She doesn't have the ear of the masses. She doesn't have the eyes of every person in the world watching her actions. But think about what she does have. She has the opportunity every single day to impact people around her. She can make a difference in their lives. She can positively impact those around her. She can cause small changes through the people she works with on those mats.

In the Impact Element of Leadership, the actions of the leader are all about the ripple effect. Every person that Lea impacts goes out into the world a changed person. Now think about the chain reaction it can cause. A class of ten yoga students each feels the impact and is inspired to do great things with their life. Each of them goes into the world and they each impact another group of people – maybe in their home or in their neighborhood or in their workplace. So, for each of the ten students, they then impact ten more people around them. And the chain reaction begins. The growth becomes exponential. And the leadership that started with little ol' Lea on a yoga mat becomes a multiplier that might just change the world after all.

The Impact Element of Leadership is aligned with the seventh chakra, known as the crown or thought chakra, which concentrates on consciousness, wisdom, magnetism, awareness, and transcendence. Lea is a leader in balance with her Impact Element of Leadership. She is a tiny pebble on the ground by a massive lake. A seemingly insignificant pebble in the grand scheme of the world. But pick that tiny pebble up and throw it into the lake and watch the ripples spread out from the epicenter. That one tiny insignificant pebble caused a massive ripple. That one tiny leader causes a massive change. When we fall into the trap of thinking about making a difference on a large scale, we will often not follow through. Too much to take on. More than we can handle. But change happens one tiny step at a time. The giant ripple that flows through the entire lake begins with one single tiny pebble that is thrown.

As leaders energized by the Impact Element of Leadership, we need to realize that leadership is not all about huge change and big missions, but rather as leaders, we should be making a ton of small changes. Things that might seem insignificant in the grand scheme of life can and will catch fire in the real world. Think about a long line of dominoes that are stood up in a maze that runs along the entire floor of your business or organization or home. In order to change all of those dominoes from standing to laying down, it begins with one simple flick of a finger. It's a tiny step. It's a tiny change. It's a minimal leadership action. But the result of that tiny flick of the finger on the first domino will cause massive change. It will cause a chain reaction one piece at a time, gaining momentum as it changes all of the dominoes.

The Impact Element of Leadership is all about awareness, enlightenment, consciousness, and the ability to reflect. To look at our lives and the impact that we can have and then to act on it. It's about change and growth and evolving. It's about a metamorphosis that begins with a single tiny action. So, the question that remains is whether you are ready to energize your Impact Element of Leadership? Are you ready to be the pebble thrown into the lake? Are you ready to flick your finger and knock over those dominoes? Are you ready to be a Yogi Leader? We think you are. And we know it all starts with one tiny first action…

Lea had come to her final pose of her routine for the morning… the Headstand Pose. It was a difficult one to master, but one that she absolutely loved. It was powerful. The pose took ultimate balance to hold perfectly still. The pose was representative of the change that she wanted to make in her life every single day and with every single person. The pose literally could turn her world upside down and let her see everything from a new perspective.

People were always telling her that she was like a clairvoyant, always able to see into their souls and tell them exactly what they needed to hear without getting any of their background info. Everybody she came across and worked with told her the same thing over and over again… "You always know exactly what to say…" Between her yoga sessions and routines, to the white board motivational sayings and mantras, to her own words in conversations with people, everybody thought she was all-knowing or some kind of psychic or she had some type of magic. But Harry Potter she was not. She was far from being all-knowing. And she definitely could not see the future through a crystal ball or anything like that. But it is what people thought because they couldn't explain her ability to know them as though she could read their inner most thoughts.

In truth, Lea had no magical powers or ability to see into their minds. The truth of the matter was that often times we as humans find what we are seeking from the world around us. We notice things that we're intending to notice. We tell ourselves things and then they happen. This isn't the magic of Harry Potter, but rather an ultra-connection to the life we are living. We find exactly what we are looking for from the world around us. If we're stuck in negative self-talk then the negative things in our lives will be what we see. It will be what we hear from others. It will be what we experience. And it will continue in an excruciating self-fulfilling cycle because the more we think negative the more we find negative. But if we're using positive self-talk, then we are going to notice the positive things. We're going to hear the positives. We're going to experience the positives. We're going to live the positive life we deserve.

So much about our life comes down to the stories we tell ourselves. So much comes down to the meditation and reflection that we do. This is the transformation that occurs. This is the transformation that Lea took in her own life. She flipped the world upside down like a Headstand Pose. She sees the world differently. She takes the time to get in tune with her inner self. She works at balancing the various sides of her life. Lea realized she had reached a level she didn't think was possible in her life. She was transforming the world around her one person at a time. Because each and every person she came across that was positively impacted returned to their own part of society and made a difference there. The ripple becomes the self-fulfilling cycle that no one could stop. And the ability to change the world begins with the action of connecting with and evolving our inner selves. As Lea always points out... change begins with me and I begin with change.

She smiled at the sound of her own mantra. She even knew exactly what to say to herself. She slowly bent herself back down to the ground and returned to her sitting meditation position. She opened her eyes to find the studio filling up with people. She looked over towards the entrance to the studio and saw her assistant there smiling at her. Many times, Lea would lose herself in her morning routine and meditation and totally lose track of all time. On those days, her employees would see her through the window and know she was in meditation mode and so they would open up the studio for her. Today was one of those days.

As Lea looked around the studio that was now quickly filling up, she saw a lot of faces she knew very well. There were others she had only seen a handful of times. And then there were the ones she had never seen before. People of different races and ethnicities, different ages and generations, different neighborhoods and communities, different interests and needs, different religions, different economic brackets, and different yoga skill levels.

Lea loved them all equally. She wanted to make a difference in each and every one of their lives. She wanted to make an impact on the world. Because that was exactly who she was... a Yogi Leader. Dedicated to the craft of helping every person find within them their own inner Yogi Leader. She was all about compassionately supporting everyone's journey to discovering the Seven Elements of Leadership in their own lives. Passionately leading a movement to change the world. It was because she believed that every single person had within them the potential to be...

The Yogi Leader

Lea smiled as she looked around the room. She stood up and moved over to her white board. She grabbed the marker and began writing the perfect mantra for the day's sessions...

I am the light and the darkness...
I am the sun and the moon...
I am the day and the night...
I am one with the universe...

I AM...

THE
YOGI LEADER

About the Authors

Leila Naderi, PhD

Dr. Naderi is an award-winning leadership consultant, entrepreneur, educator, speaker, and advanced Hatha/Sivananda yoga instructor. She holds a PhD in Leadership, MBA, and B.S. in Electrical & Electronics Engineering. Dr. Naderi has over a decade of leadership and management experience in different sectors. Her international and multicultural background, as well as her profound understanding of leadership challenges within organizations have empowered her to conduct comprehensive research and implement leadership training workshops / seminars by interweaving yoga as a way to maximize human potential and improve leadership capacity.

John J. Franey, PhD

Dr. Franey is the CEO & Founder of The Leader Mill, LLC, a leadership development company focused on transforming leadership potential into power for people of all ages. He is a former collegiate athlete at and graduate of Harvard University. He holds a PhD in Leadership Studies from the University of San Diego's School of Leadership and Education Sciences and has worked as a leadership development consultant, university researcher, leadership coach, workshop presenter, adjunct professor, and K-12 educator. For everything leadership and development, visit him at www.leadermill.com.

More from The Yogi Leader

Feeling empowered? Feeling inspired? Feeling motivated? Wanting to make some changes in your life and leadership? Wanting to make a difference in the world? Wanting to lead more with mind, body, and heart? Wanting to power up the **Seven Elements of Leadership** in your own practice? Wanting to develop your own inner Yogi Leader? Then you've come to the right place... because **The Yogi Leader** doesn't end with a single book...

The Yogi Leader offers workshops, online courses, guidebooks, assessments, and other resources focused on your development of the Seven Elements of Leadership. We welcome you to join us in an engaging, innovative, and empowering developmental opportunity that blends yoga, leadership, reflection, and mindfulness.

THE
YOGI LEADER

Made in the USA
Middletown, DE
20 November 2019